DAVID BIRD trained as an analytical chemist and entered the food manufacturing business as an analyst working with baby foods, mustard and fruit squashes. He moved into the wine trade in 1973 almost by chance, but in reality because a passion for wine was already developing. 1981 was his vintage year, becoming a Master of Wine, a Chartered Chemist and father to his first son. He specialises in quality assurance techniques, such as ISO 9000 and Hazard Analysis, and has been involved with wine activities in France, Italy, Spain, Portugal, Hungary, Denmark, Ukraine, Russia, Algeria, Australia and England.

UNDERSTANDING WINE TECHNOLOGY

A BOOK FOR THE NON-SCIENTIST
THAT EXPLAINS THE SCIENCE OF WINEMAKING

DAVID BIRD

Chartered Chemist and Master of Wine

DBQA Publishing
Great Britain

Published by DBQA Publishing

Nursery House, Askham, Newark, Nottinghamshire NG22 0RP, UK

First published in Great Britain 2000

ISBN 0 9535802 0 2

Designed by David Bird
Photography and drawings by David Bird
Printed in the UK by Warwick Printing Company Limited
Theatre Street, Warwick CV34 4DR

To Pamela Vandyke Price

A Woman of Taste
And the inspiration for this book

Wine, the most delightful of drinks, whether we owe it to Noah, who planted the vine, or to Bacchus, who pressed the juice from the grape, goes back to the childhood of the world.

BRILLAT-SAVARIN
La Physiologie du gout

Contents

Acknowledgements

The first seeds for a book explaining the science of wine in layman's language were sown in 1983 by Pamela Vandyke Price, during a tour of the Hungarian wine regions. Pamela cajoled and persuaded me for the whole of the sixteen years that it has taken to finally write the book, and it is to her that I owe the greatest debt. Not only was she the prime mover in the first instance, but she has graciously given the practical assistance that a first-time writer needed.

I am indebted to Kym Milne, a fellow Master of Wine and a renowned modern winemaker, not only for writing the Forward, but also for reading the text critically.

Grateful thanks are also due to Steve Ellis of Sartorius Limited, Keith Pryce of Seitz (UK) Ltd and Mark Bannister of Carlson Filtrations Ltd for supplying photomicrographs of filter media and micro-organisms, to Waverley Vintners Ltd for photomicrographs of yeasts and bacteria, to John Corbet-Milward of the Wine and Spirit Association for checking the contents of chapter 16, to the Royal Society of Chemistry for information about H C von Fehling, to Godfrey Spence of the Wine & Spirit Education Trust for advice on publication, and not least to my wife, Alice, for reading the script several times.

Forward

By Kym Milne MW

Have any of the following questions every concerned you:

- Why does wine contain alcohol and how does it get there?

- What are modern winemaking techniques and how do they affect the quality of wine?

- What are the pH and TA of a wine, and are they important?

- What is the difference between an earth filter, a pad filter and a membrane filter?

Understanding Wine Technology answers these questions, as well as many others of varying degrees of technicality. This book has been written with the aim of de-mystifying the technology of winemaking for the interested layman.

Master of Wine, David Bird, is ideally suited for writing such a book, as he has extensive knowledge of the technical side of winemaking, gained during many years in quality assurance in the UK wine trade. This has involved travelling the world and checking that wine producers have the appropriate technology and quality systems to satisfy the demands made upon suppliers by the extremely selective UK wine retailers.

David has extensive experience in lecturing on the twin subjects of wine technology and quality assurance to Master of Wine students and to those studying for the Diploma examination of the Wine and Spirit Education Trust.

This book is ideally suited to those who require more detailed explanations than can be obtained from the vast array of well-written "coffee table" wine books, but who, on the other hand, do not want to be bombarded with chemical formulae and the detail of a winemaking text book. Students of the many wine trade courses around the world will find it a clear and concisely written explanation of the general principles and practicalities of the technology of wine production.

INTRODUCTION

This book is aimed at the person with no formal scientific training, yet who is interested in the science behind wine and wants to know the mechanism behind the complex transformations that take place. Throughout it scientific terminology has been kept to a minimum and an attempt has been made to use everyday words and phrases. Indeed, there are places where the scientist might raise the eyebrows, places where perhaps science has had to give way to an easy understanding of a complex principle. For this I make no apologies, as I have put communication of ideas before correct scientific protocol, as this book is not intended as a learned treatise on winemaking.

Those who have had an education in the arts frequently find that anything scientific is difficult to assimilate. This is a particularly unfortunate in the world of wine, as this is one of the areas of interest where art and science come together. The modern winemaker, graduated from Roseworthy or Geisenheim or Bordeaux, to name but a few of the establishments offering advanced courses in scientific winemaking, must surely also be an artist. There must be an innate feeling for creating something of beauty, as a painter creates a beautiful picture, or a composer an interesting piece of music, so the great winemaker aims to create something which is much more than a mere beverage. Art and science become inextricably linked, which is but one of the reasons that wine is so fascinating.

The great joy of wine appreciation is the infinite variety shown by wines around the world. This is due primarily to the fact that there is no fixed route to the production of good wine. At every stage of winemaking there is a choice and at many of these points totally opposed principles are available, resulting in infinite permutations. It is the correct choice at each stage that separates the brilliant winemaker from the merely good.

This book finally came to fruition as a result of lecturing to students sitting the Diploma Examination of the Wine and Spirit Education Trust, who had complained for many years that such a book did not exist. Hopefully, it will be useful for all future Diploma students, as well as those going on to studies for the Master of Wine examination. But, above all, I would hope that all lovers of wine will find something of interest, something that will enhance their enjoyment of what is to me the world's best and most healthy beverage.

Chapter 1

THE GIFT OF NATURE

Good wine ruins the purse; bad wine ruins the stomach.

Spanish Proverb

The origins of wine

Wine, as even the most moderate of drinkers knows, varies enormously in quality, from the positively vile to heavenly nectar. Yet they are all the product of the fermentation of grape juice. The inquisitive wine drinker cannot help but question this diversity of quality and style, and wonder why there should be this wide range, when the raw material is simply the grape.

There can be little doubt that the first wine ever tasted by man was the result of an accident of nature. The vine is an ancient plant and has been known for millennia as the bearer of nutritious fruit. It is highly probable that grapes had long been gathered for consumption as fruit, or for the production of a delicious juice. All that was necessary for the discovery of wine was for a container of juice to have been left standing longer than usual, when the natural yeasts in the atmosphere or on the skins of the grapes would start a fermentation process and convert the sugars to alcohol. Initially, the juice would have been regarded as spoiled because, in its early stages, fermentation produces an odour of rot and degradation. Only on further keeping, and after a cautious tasting, would it have been discovered that a total transformation had taken place, and something had been produced with strange and wonderful properties.

This ancient wine was born without the aid of science and would have been a very hit and miss affair. Despite the work of Louis Pasteur (1822 – 1895) at the University of Lille in the middle of the nineteenth century, when he discovered that fermentation was due to the presence of micro-organisms, it was not until the last three decades of the twentieth century that scientific principles have been rigorously applied to winemaking.

The traditional way of making wine involved little science: grapes were crushed to release the juice, which was allowed to ferment with the naturally occurring micro-organisms until the juice had been converted into wine, with no temperature control and no analysis. The results were sometimes wonderful and sometimes atrocious.

The natural cycle

Winemaking is undoubtedly an art and the winemaker an artist, but if an understanding of the basics of the science that lies behind the transformation of grape juice into wine can be grasped, then the potential of the grape can be realised. The pinnacle of quality can be achieved by the application of science through quality control, used in its holistic sense: controlling quality in the vineyard itself, of the vines, of the grapes, of the expressed juice, of the fermentation process and of the finished wine.

As the grapes hang on the vine and gradually come to full maturity, with the aid of sunshine and warmth, the potential quality within the grape reaches a peak. The threat to this quality comes in the instant that man interferes and gathers the grapes. It is critically important that the quality inherent in the grape is maintained between gathering and processing because chemical and biochemical changes occur from the moment the bunch is separated from the vine.

But, more than this, maintaining the quality of the wine after it has been produced is particularly difficult because wine is a meta-stable substance; it is half-way down the slope of degradation from grape juice to water. It is the product of the microbiological attack of grape juice, the same process that reduces all living matter to water, nitrogen, carbon dioxide and a few mineral salts. In reality, wine is a small part of one of nature's cyclic processes, the carbon cycle.

In this process green plants absorb carbon dioxide from the atmosphere, converting it to sugars, which are then used to create alcohol. This, in turn gives rise to vinegar, which itself decomposes to release carbon dioxide into the atmosphere, which starts the cycle all over again.

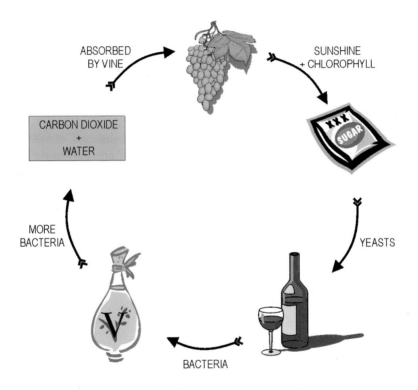

ABSORBED BY VINE

SUNSHINE + CHLOROPHYLL

CARBON DIOXIDE + WATER

MORE BACTERIA

YEASTS

BACTERIA

1.1 The production and destruction of wine

The complete cycle in detail is as follows:

1. In sunlight, the vine absorbs carbon dioxide (CO_2) from the atmosphere through the stomata in the leaves and water through its roots. With the aid of the green chlorophyll in the leaves, it converts these raw materials to sugars, which are stored in the grapes. This is the process known as photosynthesis and requires sunlight and warmth.

2. After the grapes have been picked and crushed, the yeasts convert the sugars to alcohol, with some of the carbon atoms from the sugar returning to the atmosphere as carbon dioxide.

3. The next stage is the process known as oxidation, where the wine is attacked by the oxygen of the air, with the aid of bacteria, which convert the alcohol to acetic acid, producing vinegar.

4. By the action of more bacteria the vinegar is decomposed, yielding, ultimately, water and carbon dioxide.

5. The water flows into the soil and the carbon dioxide goes into the atmosphere where they are ready for further re-cycling.

All of this activity is dependent upon the presence of enzymes, which are the key to all life processes: if they are poisoned, life ceases. The reason that cyanide is such a deadly poison is that it inactivates the enzymes in our bodies, thus stopping all our essential bodily processes and death is instantaneous. An enzyme acts as a catalyst, a substance that promotes a particular chemical reaction, but does not actually take part in it. They are large and complex molecules that are one step down from living organisms; they are not actually alive and cannot reproduce themselves, but they can easily be poisoned.

Enzymes in wine need controlling, for there are both good and bad enzymes, the good ones being responsible for the process of fermentation, the rogues (known as the oxidases) resulting in rapid oxidation. Fortunately, it is not necessary to resort to cyanide to control them, as there are many less noxious chemicals that will inactivate them, sulphur dioxide (SO_2) being the one that is widely used in winemaking.

The application of science has given the winemaker choice; at every stage of the winemaking process there are options, many of which have only become available because of scientific research. The potential for making good wine is better than ever before. Equally, never before has such a range of high quality wine been available at such low prices.

Wine and health

What a joy it is to be living in an era when we are told that wine is good for us! In the past decades we had to endure the constant warnings of the dangers of alcohol, how it is addictive, how it can damage the liver, how families are ruined by excessive drinking. These dangers are still very real and moderation remains the principle by which we should all abide. But now, at last, we know that sensible drinking is healthy.

This first came to light in 1991 in a study which came to be known by the colloquial title of The French Paradox. This was a study whose primary purpose was to demonstrate that dairy fat consumption and coronary heart disease are highly correlated. However, the paradox occurred amongst the population of a few French cities which showed that, despite a high proportion of fatty foods in their diet, the incidence of coronary heart disease was low. Further investigation indicated that the consumption of alcohol played a large part in this situation. It has been discovered that alcohol increases the high-density cholesterol, the so-called "good cholesterol" that lowers the risk of heart disease, at the same time lowering the dangerous form, the low-density cholesterol.

Red wine has recently become particularly favoured, as we know that it contains additional valuable life-prolonging agents, the flavonoids, which have two important properties relating to the prevention of heart attacks. First, they reduce the tendency for cholesterol to clog the arteries by inhibiting the oxidation of the dangerous low-density cholesterol. This is the mechanism by which arteries become clogged with fatty deposits. Second, they inhibit the aggregation of platelets, which in simple language means that there is a reduced chance of the formation of a blood clot (thrombosis).

Resveratrol is another health promoting substance that has recently been discovered in wine. It is a member of a group of compounds known as phytoalexins that are produced in plants during times of stress, such as bad weather or insect or animal attack. It can be found in many plants, but red wine has been found to be a particularly rich source. It is known to be both antioxidant and anti-mutagenic and inhibits all three phases of the cancer process: initiation, promotion and progression. Further, it would appear to give some protection against various dementias, especially Alzheimer's.

Another positive aspect of wine in relation to health is the high natural level of potassium salts that it contains, one of the highest of all foodstuffs. Potassium is valuable in counteracting excess sodium in the body. Although sodium is an element which is essential to biological functions, an excess causes an increase in blood pressure, or hypertension. Modern diets, especially snack foods and many fast foods, contain too much sodium for good health. Potassium, although chemically closely related to sodium, does not have this bad effect on blood pressure, but does have the useful property of replacing sodium in the body, the sodium being excreted in the urine.

The list of the benefits bestowed by wine seems to get longer every day: it can lower the risk of coronary heart disease, thrombosis, Alzheimer's, cancer and leukaemia, and it protects against the modern scourge of eating too much salt. Alcohol, *per se*, has a relaxing effect on the system and can be of great social value, provided it is not abused. So, let us revel in regular, moderate drinking (around two glasses of wine per day for a man, and slightly less for a woman) and gain the benefits that wine can bestow, as it is, after all, one of the oldest beverages known to mankind.

It is gratifying to note that, after ten years of health warnings on alcoholic beverages in the United States, the Bureau of Alcohol, Tobacco and Firearms (BATF) has published new regulations regarding the mandatory statements on the labels. It is now permissible to use one of the following statements:

> *'To learn the health effects of wine consumption,*
> *send for the federal government's Dietry Guide for*
> *Americans.'*

or

> *'The proud people who made this wine encourage you to consult your family doctor about the health effects of wine consumption'*

Further reading:

● Concentration of the phytoalexin resveratrol in wine. *American Journal of Enology and Viticulture,* vol. 43 p. 49-52 (1992).

● Wine, alcohol, platelets, and the French paradox for coronary heart disease. *The Lancet,* vol. 339, pp. 1523-1526 (1992).

● Beyond alcohol: Beverage consumption and cardiovascular mortality. *Clinica Chimica Acta,* vol. 237, pp. 155-187 (1995).

Chapter 2

IN THE VINEYARD

Noah, a tiller of the soil, was the first to plant the vine.

Genesis 9 20

The vine

Wine is made from grapes, and only from grapes. This may sound a somewhat dogmatic statement, especially to those who are used to making 'wine' from apples, raspberries, currants, rhubarb, nettles, or indeed any edible fruit, vegetable or leaf. Such products must be named after the substance from which they are made, such as 'Apple Wine'.

Grapes are the fruit of the vine, which is a member of a large family of climbing plants, only a few of which are suitable for making wine. The study of the vine is known as ampelography, coming from the Greek *ampelos*, which means, not surprisingly, the vine.

The **family** to which the vine belongs is known as *Vitaceae*, plants which show a tendency towards trailing and twining. This is a large family of 11 genera, but by far the most important is the **genus** V*itis*, the grape vines, although another well-known genus is *Parthenocissus*, the genus to which the Virginia Creeper and Boston Ivy belong.

The genus vitis contains some 60 different species, not many of which are suitable for the production of grapes for making wine. The most important **species** by far is *V. vinifera*, the European grape vine. Other species of use in winemaking are *V. labrusca*, the North American fox grape, *V. riparia*, the riverbank grape, *V. aestivalis*, the summer grape and *V. rotundifolia*, the muscadine grape. *V. vinifera* is the only species that gives rise to wine of a flavour which is acceptable around the world, but some of the other species are important in providing root-stocks on which to graft the European vine in the fight against phylloxera.

The single species of *V. vinifera* contains numerous **varieties**, probably around one thousand, many with well-known names such as Cabernet Sauvignon and Chardonnay, probably the two most widespread of the international varieties.

The selection of the right vine does not end with the choice of a variety, for it is now possible to select **clones** of many of the better known varieties. This use of the word clone is somewhat misleading, its true meaning being an identical copy. In the case of vines, it actually means the selection of a particular vine that has characteristics that set it apart from the majority. It is possible to select clones specially bred for high quality, or for disease resistance, or even for high yield with the inevitable accompanying low quality (although there are some viticulturaltists who could claim that high yield with high quality is attainable).

2.1 The family tree of the grape vine

Genetic modification is an obvious step to be taken at some time in the future. The vine is a delicate plant, subject to attack by many agents, such as moulds, mildews and viruses. A vine which has a built-in resistance towards such troubles would be widely received – but only after a sane and balanced attitude towards GM plants has been established.

Grafting and rootstocks

It must be to the permanent shame of England that the pestilence of *Phylloxera vestatrix* was introduced to Europe via Kew Gardens, albeit unwittingly. Vine plants brought over from America in the nineteenth century for experimental purposes were carrying an infestation of Phylloxera, which rapidly spread throughout Europe, destroying many of the long-established vineyards by attacking the roots.

After many desperate measures were taken to eradicate the pest, such as flooding the vineyards, or treating with hydrogen sulphide (a particularly noxious and dangerous chemical), it was beaten by sheer logic. Scientific detective work traced the origin of the pest to America, where it was living happily with the American native vines. This being the case, it seemed a logical step to graft the European vine on to American rootstock, with complete success.

Grafting has actually yielded a positive benefit, in that it is possible to select a suitable rootstock for matching the vine to the soil. In rich soils a weak rootstock can be used; in chalky soils an alkaline-resistant rootstock is chosen. The choice of rootstock is now regarded as important as the variety of the vine itself.

Underground conditions

The basic principle of growing grapes for winemaking is to force the vine to develop a large underground system of roots that deliver an ample supply of minerals and nutrients to the growing leaf system, where the sugars are being generated by photosynthesis. All of these components are eventually transported to the grapes, which act as storehouses. Vigorous pruning of the above ground system ensures that these substances are concentrated into a small number of grapes. In rich soil the vine produces enormous top growth from a small root system and the grapes never reach the intensity of flavour that is required for good wine.

There can be no denying that the vine reacts in a similar way to humans in relation to performance: the best results are obtained when subjected to a certain degree of stress. The idle and cosseted person merely gets fat and rarely produces anything of interest and, similarly, the vine in rich soil yields much foliage and fat grapes, which produce dull wine. In well-drained poor soil the vine is forced to develop a large root system which penetrates deep into the subsoil in search of moisture and nutrition, and in so doing it picks up an abundance of minerals that find their way into the grapes.

In common with many other herbaceous plants, the vine has no tap root, but has a large number of fine feeding roots which can burrow down tens of metres into the subsoil when forced to do so by lack of moisture. The drainage of a vineyard is one of the major influences in the production of quality grapes. It was discovered some years ago that the difference in quality along the gravel slopes of the Médoc was due largely to the proximity of small streams and man-made drainage channels that allow the water to flow out of the gravel, the best vineyards being the most well drained.

Although the importance of good drainage is widely accepted, the effect on quality of the various soil types is not fully understood, probably because the vine will tolerate a wide range. The broad principles that have emerged are that alkaline soils emphasise the characteristics of white grapes, as in Sancerre and Champagne, and gravel soils produce particularly good red wines, as exemplified by the Médoc. But the relationship between soil and vine variety is far from rigid, and fine wines are produced around the world on various combinations of soil and vine.

The concentration of essential elements in the juice is also related to the density of planting. The underlying principle is to make the vine act as a concentrating plant, gathering the minerals and flavour precursors from a large volume of strata and sub-strata and concentrating them into a small number of grapes. Planting density provides a useful way of controlling the division of the available resources in the soil among the right number of plants. In a rich soil, vines are planted closer together, resulting in competition for the nutrients, which makes the roots delve deep into the sub-soil.

Above the ground

The balance between sugars and acids in the ripe grape plays an important part in the quality of the finished wine. This balance is determined by the degree of sunshine that the grape receives during the growing season, which is defined at a basic level by the climate: with too much sun the acids fall too low and the sugars climb too high, resulting in a flabby alcoholic wine. Conversely, too little sun gives a thin, sharp wine, and possibly with insufficient alcohol even to be called wine, because the EU regulations for table wine set a minimum limit of 8.5% for the alcohol produced from the natural sugars.

2.2 Bush vines

2.3 Pergola vines

Given that it is not within our power to control the climate, we can influence the ripening of the grapes by paying attention to microclimate and by the careful choice of elevation and aspect (the direction in which the vineyard faces, relative to the sun).

Microclimate plays a significant part in the successful production of wine in many parts of the world, either by reducing the effect of the sun by going up to higher altitudes, or, in areas which suffer from a deficiency of sunshine, by using slopes of the right aspect to make better use of the sun's rays, especially during the morning or the late afternoon.

The various shapes into which a vine can be trained give us another way of controlling the effect of heat on the ripening of the grapes. The arrangement of the leaves forms what is known as the canopy of the vine. The manipulation of this canopy, or canopy management, is particularly important in marginal climates, where the different styles of training can be used to either maximise or minimise the effect of the sun's rays. In vineyards such as Châteauneuf-du-Pape the effect of the sun is deliberately emphasised by training the vines in the bush style, with short stems, so that the producing parts of the vine are close to the ground. This traps the maximum warmth from the sun's rays, both directly and from the reflected heat from the 'pudding stones'. This effect continues into the night, when the stones act as gigantic storage heaters, enveloping the vines with warm air.

In hot climates where a lighter, crisper wine is wanted, the vines are trained high, with their upper branches formed into a pergola. In these conditions, the grapes hang down underneath the foliage and remain in the comparative cool of the shade.

Conversely, in a cool marginal climate such as England, much use is made of specialised training methods such as the Geneva Double Curtain, where the ratio of foliage to grapes is carefully controlled to give the maximum exposure to sunlight and, thus, the maximum production of sugar.

The principle of maintaining the concentration of the flavour elements in the juice applies equally to the annual round of pruning. This needs to be severe, so that the sparse supply of the precious constituents is not spread too widely over a large number of bunches, but shared between the lucky few. Grapes are the basic material from which wine is made, and the potential quality of the ultimate wine is already present in the grape juice. This quality must be preserved throughout the winemaking process. The adage "Fine wine is created in the vineyard" is very true. Or, again, "It is easy to make bad wine from good grapes, but you cannot make good wine from bad grapes".

Chapter 3

PRINCIPAL CONSTITUENTS OF GRAPES

My friend had a vineyard on a fertile hillside . . .
He expected it to yield grapes, but sour grapes were all that it gave.

Isaiah 5 1-2

Grape juice supplies all of the components of wine that give it its ultimate quality and style. The winemaker can influence the final balance, but he cannot add quality, if it is not there in the first place. The balance of the principal constituents in the grape juice is of prime importance to the style of the finished wine. Too much sunshine and heat will yield a wine that is highly intoxicating, and short on acidity – hot and flabby. The converse produces an unpleasant, thin and acidic concoction that is fit only for distillation (and, incidentally, might make a wonderful base wine for the production of a top-flight brandy). Balance is a word used frequently throughout the production and tasting of wine, because it is the all-important balance of the major components of juice that yields an attractive wine.

Sugars

In common with most fruits, unripe grapes contain low levels of sugars and a high concentration of acidssugars: sunshine and warm conditions are required for the production of adequate sugars by the process of photosynthesis. Throughout the growing season, sugars are manufactured in the leaves of the vine and are transported through the plant to the grapes, which act as storehouses. At the same time flavour components are formed in both the skin and the pulp. The sugars are present mainly as glucose and fructose, which are the natural sugars of many fruits. These two sugars are virtually identical in characteristics, and indeed have the same chemical formula $C_6H_{12}O_6$. The only difference is in the shape of the molecules, where one is the mirror image of the other. Sucrose, which is the sugar present in sugar beet or sugar cane, is virtually absent from grapes.

The first of the many decisions that have to be made in the vinification process is getting the right balance between sugars and acids by following the process of maturation of the grapes.

In the days before science came to the aid of the winemaker the maturation was judged purely by the experienced palate. When grapes are immature, they taste bitter due to unripe tannins, sharp due to excess acidity, and they have insufficient sugar to counteract these harsh components. At maturity, the grapes will taste delicious, if somewhat more concentrated than table grapes. Nowadays, even the most inexperienced can determine the progress of maturity in a very exact and scientific way by measuring the rise of sugar with a pocket refractometer, a simple instrument which measures the refractive index of the juice. This instrument is particularly simple to use, as the internal scale gives a direct reading of the sugar content of the juice.

3.1 Using a refractometer

To use the refractometer, the glass prisms in the base of the instrument are opened and a few drops of juice are placed on the lower prism. The prisms are shut and the instrument held up to the light, as if it were a telescope. A scale graduated in sugar concentration can be seen, with a line of shadow cutting across the scale, giving a direct reading. These daily readings can be plotted on a graph, showing the rise in sugar concentration, which gives an indication of the right moment of harvesting.

The perennial problem is the lottery of the weather. If the sugar level is low, further ripening on the vine might result in an increase in the sugar content; but if it rains, the sugar concentration might fall, as a result of dilution. The correct judgement at this moment lies with the expertise of the winemaker.

Acids

The second principal component of all fruits is the acids. Grapes contain natural acids, which impart freshness and keeping qualities to the finished wine, and are an essential component of the taste of all wines. In unripe grapes the predominant acid is malic acid, which is the main acid of apples (L. *malus* = apple), and is a very sharp tasting acid.

As the grape ripens, tartaric acid becomes the principal acid. Salts of this acid form the major proportion of the deposits found in containers after the storage of wine (L. *tartarum* = deposit). Tartaric and malic acids together constitute over 90% of the acidity of the grape.

The chemical formulae of tartaric and malic acids are closely related, so it is perhaps not surprising that the two acids are easily transmuted, one to the other:

Tartaric acid   HOOC.CHOH.CHOH.COOH

Malic acid   HOOC.CHOH.CH$_2$.COOH

The process of ripening is complex, with many different mechanisms coming into play. Not only are the sugars being manufactured from carbon dioxide and water, but the acidity within the grape goes down. This fall is due in part to the dilution of the acids by the large quantity of sugars that are being transported to the grape, but also to the biochemical conversion of malic acid to sugars, which may seem surprising. Biochemistry is capable of many seemingly miraculous transformations. During this stage, it is the malic acid that is being lost, the concentration of tartaric acid falling only slightly.

At a later stage of wine production, after the alcoholic fermentation, the malic acid can undergo another biochemical conversion, this time with the aid of a bacterium and known as the malo-lactic fermentation. In this case the very acidic malic acid is converted into lactic acid, a softer and more gentle acid. This is the acid formed in sour milk (L. *lac* = milk) (See p.66).

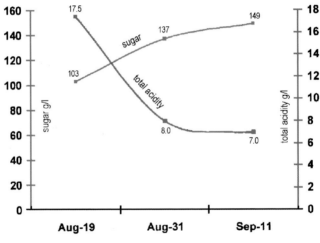

3.2 Evolution of sugars and acids

The right moment for picking depends largely on the balance between sugars and acids being optimal, and this balance will vary according to the style of the wine being produced. In hot climates, where the acid concentration drops at an alarming rate as maturity approaches, picking might take place slightly early. In cool climate conditions, however, the harvest is often left as late as possible, to allow the acids to decrease to an acceptable level. In the graph above it can be seen how the acids have dropped from 17.5 g/litre to 8 g/litre in twelve days, during which time the sugars have risen from 103 g/litre to 137 g/litre. In this instance, the graph also shows that there is little to be gained by leaving the grapes on the vine after the end of August, as the principal changes have already taken place.

Minerals

Grape juice is rich in many different minerals, picked up by the roots of the vine as they delve deep into the subsoil in search of moisture. The most abundant of these by a factor of at least ten is potassium (K), which is something of a double-edged sword. On the one hand, it is a valuable mineral, conferring on wine health-giving properties. On the other it is the cause of many problems relating to tartrate crystals, for it is potassium bi-tartrate that precipitates in bottles, resulting in consumer complaints.

The next most abundant mineral is calcium (Ca), which also plays a part in tartrate crystal formation. Other minerals include magnesium (Mg), with iron (Fe) and copper (Cu) at even lower levels, and traces of many others.

The total mineral content of the juice plays an important role in conjunction with the acids, with which the minerals form salts, controlling the acid taste of the finished wine in the mouth. (See pH on p.149)

Due to the presence of these minerals in the juice, much of the tartaric acid exists as tartrate salts in solution. After fermentation, the alcohol reduces the solubility of the tartrates to such a degree that their solution in the wine becomes 'super-saturated', meaning that they should crystallise out. However, this does not usually happen immediately because of the presence of colloidal matter (see below), which prevents crystallisation. After a period of time, when these colloids have de-natured and lost their protective property, the tartrates crystallise out and form a deposit. This occurs naturally during the long-term storage of wines in vat or cask, as witness the tremendous crystalline deposits inside older casks. This is the origin of the name of tartaric acid, *tartar* being the Latin for deposit.

The physical properties of the potassium and calcium tartrates are quite different. The potassium salt is actually potassium hydrogen tartrate, or potassium bi-tartrate, otherwise known as cream of tartar, as used in baking powder. This substance crystallises relatively easily, because its solubility decreases as the temperature falls. It forms fairly large crystals, which can sometimes be mistaken for broken glass. (See p.191)

Calcium tartrate, on the other hand, is more difficult to eliminate because its solubility hardly changes with a decrease in temperature. In fact, it is slightly more soluble at low temperatures, so refrigerating the wine has little effect. Unfortunately, it is still subject to the protecting effect of colloids, so can precipitate in the bottle when the colloids have denatured, when it comes down as very small crystals, looking like common salt, or even a snow storm, when shaken up.

(See page 119 for tartrate stabilisation processes)

Polyphenols

There is more to the maturation of the grape than merely the change in the acid/sugar balance, as it also involves many other processes, including changes to the polyphenols in the skins. These polyphenols are a complex group of substances, otherwise known as flavonoids, which include tannins, and the anthocyanins, the colouring compounds.

Tannins are a widely distributed group of compounds, found in many plant materials. Probably the best-known sources are tea and rhubarb, whose drying effect on the palate is well known. In grapes, they are found not only in the skins, but also in the stems and pips. As these tannins are loosely bound into the structure of these parts of the vine material, it is possible, by various means of manipulation to control the tannin content of the extracted juice. Stems are rich in tannins, so leaving them in contact with the juice during the maceration process results in a juice with higher tannin content. If, on the other hand, the skins and juice already contain an adequate supply of tannins, de-stemming is carried out, on either the total crop, or a proportion of it.

As maturity approaches, the chemical composition of the polyphenols in the skin changes, with the result that the harsh and very bitter tannins in the unripe grape become softer and more approachable.

The anthocyanins are one of the groups of compounds responsible for the colour of fruits and flowers and have fascinating names and different colours reflecting their occurrence in plants: malvidin (mallow), delphinidin (delphiniums), peonidin (peonies), petunidin (petunias) and cyanidin (cornflowers). They are found mainly in the skin of the grape and are responsible for its colour. During maturation of the wine the ratio of these various anthocyanins changes, the proportion of the blue-coloured compounds diminishing, hence the gradation from purple-red to orange with age.

The depth of colour of red and rosé wines depends entirely on the way in which these substances are extracted from the skins during the fermentation process. In traditional fermentation, the alcohol produced by the yeast extracts the anthocyanins from the skins, thick skins yielding more colouring matter than thin skins. This extraction can also be achieved by the effect of heat, which breaks down the cell walls (see *thermovinification, p.77*).

Recent research has shown the flavonoids to be an extremely important group of compounds, particularly in relation to the human body and health. The ageing of the body is largely due to oxidation and, hence, the presence of antioxidants in the diet is regarded as essential, which is the reason that vitamins are important, as several of the vitamins are antioxidants. Some members of the flavonoid group are also powerful antioxidants and others have the valuable property of preventing the clumping of platelets in the blood, which minimises the possibility of coronary heart disease. Thus it can be seen that these flavonoids confer on wine that precious quality of 'being good for you', actually slowing the process of ageing. This applies particularly to red wines, as they contain higher levels of polyphenols than white or rosé wines. Hence, the recommendation that two to three glasses of red wine per day are beneficial!

Proteins & colloids

Some of the most complex molecules in grape juice are the proteins and other colloids that are essential to the health of the grape. Proteins are built up from amino acids, which are the basic building blocks of all organic life. Because of the size of their molecules, which are larger than simple matter such as sugar or salt by a factor of around a thousand times, they are classified as colloids. They are nutritious, both to yeasts and to the ultimate consumer, but they have one drawback, in that they cause the wine to become hazy or even cloudy after a certain period of time, a period which can vary greatly from a few weeks to many months.

Colloids have very complicated molecular structures, with molecules that appear under the electron microscope as tangled chains of carbon, hydrogen, oxygen and nitrogen atoms. Some of these colloids are totally stable and never change their properties. Others, known as the unstable colloids, slowly change their nature as their molecules re-arrange themselves (known as denaturing) and cause deposits in the finished wine. In old-style winemaking this occurs naturally during the long period of maturation in the cask. But the speed with which modern wine is rushed through the process necessitates the removal of unstable proteins by the treatment known as 'fining', which is explained on p.99.

Nutrients and flavour components

There are vast numbers of other minor constituents in the grape which contribute to the ultimate quality and flavour of the wine. Proteins and amino acids, the building blocks of proteins, provide sources of nitrogen for the growing yeasts during fermentation. Glycerol (glycerine), a slightly sweet tasting syrupy substance when in concentrated form, is present partly in the original juice, but is also formed during fermentation and confers a smoothness and body to the finished wine.

All of these substances play a large part in the formation of complex flavours by inter-reacting and producing a vast number of new compounds during the maturation process of the wine.

There are, however, many other substances that contribute to the fruity taste of wine and form what is known as the 'primary aroma' of the wine, giving it its varietal character. These compounds are contained in cells which form the inner surface of the skin, hence the importance of the skin and the role it plays during the processing of the grape. The close association of these aroma compounds with the skin of the grape has encouraged many winemakers to experiment with various forms of skin contact, especially with white grapes, in order to extract maximum flavour and character.

It is the concentration of all these components that creates fine wines. The complexity of these components makes it almost impossible to define the quality of a wine in terms of chemical analysis. The simple analysis of Château Latour of a good vintage, for example, would be identical to that of a basic vin de table. The difference lies not in the alcohol, or the total acidity, or any of the other basic components, but in the myriad minor constituents that make up the flavour of the wine. These are mainly complex esters and higher alcohols with long and difficult names, such as isobutyl acetate and ethyl 2-carboxyfuranoate (using old nomenclature), many of them present at infinitesimal concentrations.

If it were important to reduce the assessment of quality to chemical terms, it would be necessary to expand the analysis to include several hundred compounds, a very expensive and time-consuming task. Even the new 'mechanical noses' that have been invented find it impossible to differentiate the vast range of qualities that are available. A trained taster is able to do the job much more quickly and more cheaply, and the wine gives pleasure in the process – which, after all, was the original intention of the winemaker!

Chapter 4

THE ROLE OF OXYGEN

Democracies must try to find ways to starve the terrorist and the hijackers of the oxygen of publicity on which they depend.

Margaret Thatcher 1985

The atmosphere in which we live, the air that we breathe, is composed approximately of four-fifths nitrogen (N_2) and one-fifth oxygen (O_2). The nitrogen of the atmosphere, although critical for life, is relatively unreactive. It requires the efforts of nitrifying bacteria on the roots of leguminous plants to convert it to nitrates and other nitrogen compounds which can then be used by plants to produce amino acids, the building blocks of organic life. The amino acids are then assembled into proteins, a group of substances critical to all life, the name deriving from the Greek *proteios* meaning "holding first place".

Oxygen plays an entirely different role, and one that is somewhat ambivalent, in that it both supports and destroys life. From the early days of our education, we are taught that oxygen is the staff of life. Oxygen enables fires to burn; oxygen enables our bodies to metabolise food and release energy. Life as we know it could not exist without oxygen. However, there is another side to the story, because oxygen is also the main element involved in degradation and ageing. Millions of years ago, when life was first emerging, the Earth's atmosphere contained a high proportion of hydrogen sulphide (H_2S), a gas that is highly toxic to life as we know it today, and oxygen was total anathema. Ever since primitive life took the route in its development towards an atmosphere containing oxygen, we have had to defend ourselves against its effects. Oxygen is destructive and needs constant control.

Old-style winemaking

Before the days of scientific training, the traditional winemaker would probably have been unaware of the dangers of oxygen, and would not have taken precautions to prevent its effect. Grapes were pressed in the presence of air; the juice would have picked up plenty of oxygen on its way to the fermentation vessel, and the finished wine would have been moved several times during the clarification process, gathering oxygen at every opportunity. Much of the time, no great harm was done and good wine might well have been produced. The good winemaker will have understood where the dangers lie and will have used his experience and expertise to avoid disaster. But this technique is more art than science and a combination of oxygen and 'bugs' could wreak havoc.

There are times when traditional winemaking is totally appropriate, as in the production of some sherries and the wines of Tokaj, where a certain degree of oxidation is essential to the traditional character of the wine. But even here, oxidation has to be kept under control, as the pathway to destruction is already being trod.

Anaerobic winemaking

Modern winemaking techniques are strictly anaerobic, meaning without oxygen. Great care is taken to prevent the ingress of oxygen at all stages because it is regarded as the destroyer of fruit in the wine. The prevention of oxidation is not difficult and merely needs good discipline throughout the winemaking process. It starts in the vineyard, when the gathered grapes are dusted with an antioxidant powder that liberates sulphur dioxide (SO_2) and prevents oxidation of the juice that exudes from every split berry.

The next step is to prevent the contact of air with the grape juice after it has been pressed out, by flushing all tanks and pipelines with a so-called 'inert' gas such as carbon dioxide or nitrogen, which removes the air, and thus the oxygen. More sulphur dioxide is added to the grape juice itself, to neutralise any oxygen that might have found a way in. Although a rather nasty chemical in high concentration, sulphur dioxide is harmless when used at the correct level of around 100 parts per million (ppm).

Every time the finished wine is moved from vat to vat, or receives any treatment, care is taken to prevent oxygen dissolving. Oxygen dissolved in wine actually reacts quite slowly when left to its own devices, requiring assistance in the form of catalyst to hasten the reaction. Unfortunately, there are plenty of natural catalysts in the form of oxidising enzymes, the oxidases, which are ready to assist. Other catalysts, in the form of metal ions also act as catalysts to oxidation. One of the worst is copper, hence the banning of all copper or bronze equipment in a modern winery.

The positive role of oxygen

It would be wrong to think of oxygen as totally destructive, for there are a few occasions when its action is beneficial.

It is good practice to saturate grape juice with oxygen when it is being prepared for fermentation, because this gives the yeast a 'kick start' into action. When yeasts are in an oxygen-rich environment they reproduce more rapidly and can therefore build up a large population quickly, which results in a prompt start to the fermentation. (See chapter 7)

Wines made by the anaerobic method are superbly clean and fresh, and full of youthful fruit, yet risk being boring by being too perfect. This is another area where the art of the winemaker comes into play, by knowing how to apply the many other means of adding character and preventing the wine tasting like the product of a wine 'factory'. A controlled amount of oxidation undoubtedly adds to the complexity and character of the wine.

Oxygen plays an important role in the maturation of red wines in wood. Much of the character of fine red Bordeaux wines, for example, depends on the period of time they spend in oak barrels (Fr. *barriques*). During their sojourn in the barrels, the oxygen that gets in through the pores of the wood, and during the process of racking, attacks the tough tannins in the wine, causing them to precipitate and fall to the bottom of the barrels, leaving the wine softer and more supple. (See chapter 13)

Hyperoxidation

Despite the dire warnings about the destructive effects of oxygen, another technique is sometimes used that actually encourages the process of oxidation. This is one of the intriguing facts about the study of winemaking, where diametrically opposite techniques can be used and, indeed, this is the reason why it is important to understand the science behind these principles.

Hyperoxidation is a technique that involves the deliberate oxidation of the must before fermentation, something which might be regarded as anathema to a modern winemaker. During this process, oxidation is deliberately allowed to take place, which destroys the more susceptible components of the juice, resulting in a finished wine that is more stable towards oxygen.

Hyperoxidation is carried out by bubbling air through the expressed juice, without the addition of any protective additives, such as sulphur dioxide. Results from the use of this technique have confirmed that wines made by this method are indeed more stable and have a longer life. A large producer of wines in the south of France has virtually doubled the shelf-life of its delicate rosé wine since adopting the hyperoxidation technique.

However, this is not a process that should be adopted casually, in the expectation of producing a highly stable, fruity wine at the first attempt. The skill lies in knowing how much oxidation to allow before commencing the fermentation. Too much oxidation results in a destruction of the fruit which is at the heart of the wine. Even when correctly applied the process is somewhat dramatic, with the must turning the colour of black coffee and all appearing to have been lost. However, during fermentation, which is a reductive process (the reverse of oxidation), some of the oxidation of the must is reversed, and the colour returns to normal. But this reversal of oxidation is not total, and the most susceptible components of the juice are permanently destroyed – hence the improved stability of the finished wine.

Chapter 5

THE PRODUCTION OF JUICE

No grape that's kindly ripe, could be
So round, so plump, so soft as she,
Nor half so full of juice.

Ballad: Upon a Wedding
Sir John Suckling 1609 – 41

In the days before the introduction of scientific principles to the art of winemaking, grapes were harvested when they tasted sweet and fleshy, and they were crushed without undue delay by the action of the human foot. Sometimes this crushing was achieved, as in the production of port, by the naked foot, which proved to be ideal for the purpose, being firm yet gentle in action. In other areas, such as Jerez, special boots were worn, with nails projecting from the sole, to prevent the pips from being crushed and thereby releasing their bitter contents. These old practices have not entirely died out, but their use tends to be more for marketing than for practical reasons.

Pressing was always carried out in a traditional basket press, because this was the only design available, with all of its attendant problems. The tedious and slow manipulation was of no consequence, there being ample labour and time in plentiful supply.

With increased volumes and the greater influence of accountants and scientists, the situation had to change. Developments in machinery meant better and quicker crushing and pressing operations. New processes, such as flotation and hyperoxidation, were introduced. The modern winemaker has a vast repertoire of techniques from which to choose, with the possibility of producing better wine, more cheaply than ever before.

Harvesting the grapes

As the time for harvesting draws near a major decision has to be made regarding the method of picking. This is a comparatively easy decision, for there are only the two alternatives, picking by hand or by machine. The parameters to be considered are based on a combination of quality considerations, speed, economics and feasibility.

Hand picking is essential where the selection of the finest quality grapes is paramount. The great sweet wines, such as Sauternes, Tokaji Aszu or Beerenauslesen depend upon the selection of individual noble-rotted berries. These vineyards have to be traversed several times over to gather the grapes one by one, when the action of botrytis cinerea has shrivelled the grapes to their peak of condition. Human labour is again called upon if whole bunches are required, e.g. for carbonic maceration (see p.78), or when the stalks are needed for added tannin. The disadvantage of this traditional way of gathering in the harvest is the length of time it takes, even with a large band of pickers – and it is expensive.

5.1 Picking by hand

The machine harvester comes into its own as the size of the operation increases, but the greatest advantage of the machine is its speed, ensuring the gathering of the grapes when they are in their peak of condition. This includes harvesting during the night, which is particularly helpful in hot climates, when the grapes can be gathered at their coolest, thus minimising deterioration and reducing the cost of cooling the juice before fermentation. In fact, night harvesting has almost become the norm in hot climates and large vineyards, as are found in Australia and California, where grapes are often transported hundreds of miles to the winery.

There are, however, severe constraints in the use of mechanical harvesters because these monsters can only operate in specially planted vineyards and on flat land. The grapes are gathered by violent shaking of the vines, which causes them to fall off, leaving the stalks attached to the plant. This ripping action tears the skins and exposes some of the pulp to the atmosphere, so protection against oxidation is important. There can be no selection of grapes, and there are no stalks, as these will have been left on the vine. Neither can the grapes be used for the carbonic maceration process (see p.78), because whole bunches of undamaged grapes are required for this purpose.

5.2 Machine harvesting

That having been said, mechanical harvesting is widespread and is gaining in popularity, because its advantages of speed and convenience outweigh the shortcomings. Despite the denial by some of the owners of classed growth chateaux regarding the use of mechanical harvesters in Bordeaux, over 2956 such machines were in operation in the Gironde during the 1997 harvest. In common with many other techniques, the achievement of good quality comes not from the technique itself, but from the way it is handled.

Whole grapes, when first picked, are relatively stable and can be kept for a while before processing (see *Skin contact* below). But, of course, many grapes are damaged during the harvesting process, releasing some of the juice, which is not stable and is readily oxidised by the oxygen of the atmosphere, especially as the oxidising enzymes are active. The usual technique, therefore, is for pressing to take place as soon as possible, hence the tradition of building wineries in the middle of vineyards.

Preventative measures have to be taken at this early stage to avoid loss of quality by oxidation. It is a common sight to see grapes being dusted with a sulphur dioxide compound, probably potassium metabisulphite (note the spelling – not metabisulph<u>a</u>te), to knock out the enzymes and slow down the oxidation. Potassium metabisulphite is a very useful compound, being a white powder, easily packed into paper sacks and quite stable provided it is kept dry. The instant it comes into contact with water, it dissolves and releases sulphur dioxide, especially if the liquid is slightly acid, which is the case with grape juice.

De-stemming

Stems are a rich source of tannins and can be used to raise tannin levels by including them in the maceration process. If there is already a sufficiency of tannins in the grapes, the stalks from all or part of the crop can be removed by a de-stemming machine (Fr. *égrappoir*). However, this does result in a more difficult pressing operation because the stalks act as useful drainage channels. A technique sometimes used to improve drainage is to de-stem the whole crop and then to pack the press with alternate layers of grapes and stalks, which produces an easily drained mass.

The de-stemming machine is simple in design and operation, consisting of a rotating, perforated drum, with contra-rotating blades inside the drum.

5.3 De-stemming machine

The bunches of grapes are fed into the rotating drum, where the blades tumble the bunches vigorously, causing the berries to fall off and ultimately to fall out through the holes, leaving the stalks inside the drum. The grapes fall on to a conveyor belt, which transports them to the winery, and the stalks pass out through the end of the drum, from which they are collected.

The stalks that have been removed are sometimes simply dried and burned as fuel, but more ecologically minded winemakers have discovered that stalks contain sufficient sugars to make it worthwhile to subject them to further processing. The stalks are chopped and soaked in water to extract the sugars, which are then fermented to produce a weakly alcoholic liquor. This is subsequently distilled to give a high quality spirit of vegetable origin and, as such, can be used for fortification purposes. (Alcohol of mineral origin, such as is distilled during petroleum preparation, is not permitted for use in foodstuffs.)

Crushing the grapes

The next part of all winemaking operations is crushing the grapes to obtain the juice. In days gone by, and still current in some areas of world, this was achieved by the human foot, clad or un-clad. This is a totally satisfactory way of releasing the juice, the bare foot being a gentle implement for this purpose, with no danger of cracking the pips, which contain a bitter oil and astringent tannins. It was for this reason that the specially made boots that used to be used in regions such as Jerez in Andalucia were equipped with nails under the soles to prevent close contact with the bottom of the crushing trough.

Nowadays, mechanised methods of crushing are used to increase the speed of the operation. Although deceptively simple, the crusher incorporates considerable experience in its design. The crushing process must be carefully managed, as the objective is to release the free-run juice and to reduce the solid parts of the grape to the correct condition for fermentation and maceration, whilst avoiding damage to the pips. The skins must not be torn away from the pulp, because this affects the extraction of aromas from the skin cells. The stalks, if present, must not be torn open, because too much harsh tannin would be released. For these reasons, the rotating parts of crushing machines are carefully designed and have an adjustable gap between them of around three millimetres, to ensure that the grapes are not reduced to a purée.

It is worth noting that crushing and pressing are quite distinct processes, used for two different purposes. Crushing amounts to nothing more than ripping the grape apart to allow the free-run juice to flow out. The rollers in the crusher are not in contact with each other and pressure plays no part in the process. Pressing, on the other hand, is the extraction of the remaining juice which is contained in tougher cells situated nearer to the skin of the grape, and can only be released by rupturing the cells under pressure.

5.4 Crusher or fouloir

During the crushing operation the free-run juice, which is held in large and somewhat fragile cells occupying most of the volume of the grape, is liberated. This juice is of high quality and contains the lowest tannin level, because very few skin cells are fractured during the crushing process.

A comparatively new technique for releasing more juice from the pulp is the use of pectolytic enzymes, which break down the gelatinous pectins in the pulp, thus releasing more juice from the sticky mass.

Skin contact

In the making of white wine, it was, and still is, normal practice to separate the juice from the skins as quickly as possible, because it was recognised that the flavour could be spoiled by contact with the skins, which contain harsh and bitter polyphenols. As the study of winemaking advanced, it was realised that many of the flavouring components of aromatic grapes are contained in the layer of cells under the skin, which is immediately adjacent to the pulp. After the grape has been picked, provided the skin is still in contact with the juice cells, these flavour compounds gradually leach into the juice. It is therefore necessary to allow a certain amount of time for this to happen, which is contrary to the accepted technique of rapid processing.

The usual method of skin contact, or *macération pelliculaire*, as this part of the process is known, is to crush the grapes carefully and then leave the crushed mass to stand for several hours with the skins in contact with the free run juice. Reducing the temperature minimises the risk of extracting unwanted flavours because these compounds are less soluble at lower temperatures. Keeping the mixture of skins and juice for as long as two days at zero degrees Celsius (32°F) is sometimes used to bring out the maximum flavour, the low temperature preventing bitterness developing.

An alternative technique, requiring carefully gathered and undamaged bunches of grapes, involves simply leaving the grapes in a cool place overnight before crushing and pressing the next day. This somewhat subtle process results in a diffusion of the aroma compounds from the cells on the inside of the skins, whilst avoiding any contact with the exterior surface and minimising the release of polyphenols. It is essential that the grapes should be in as perfect a condition as possible, to minimise damage due to oxidation.

Red wine, of course, gets its colour from the skins of black grapes, usually during the fermentation. For the sake of clarity of definition, this is usually referred to as maceration or skin fermentation. The expression skin contact, or *macération pelliculaire,* is reserved for the production of white wines (not to be confused with *macération carbonique*, which is used in the production of red wines, see p.78).

Draining the juice

The separation of the free-run juice is important in the making of white wine, because the manner of the separation has an effect on the quality of the wine. The secret of good draining is to minimise the disturbance of the skins, to prevent the extraction of harsh polyphenols. The best method is the static drainer, where the juice can percolate gently through the mass of skins, without any disturbance. This method can, however, pose a problem of through-put in a large winery, because the draining process is slower than the other stages. For this reason, mechanical drainers have been introduced, consisting simply of a rotating archimedes screw in a horizontal tank with a perforated base. The screw rotates once every two or three minutes, gradually pushing the grapes through the machine, allowing them to drain as they go. Whilst overcoming the lack of speed of the static drainer, the disturbance of the skins does result in a greater release of the polyphenolic substances.

5.5 Draining machine

Pressing the skins

In the making of white wine, pressing comes next because it is necessary to release the remainder of the juice, which is held in the smaller, stronger cells which make up the inner layer of the skin. At the same time more polyphenols and aroma compounds are released.

In the production of red wine, this part of the process comes after fermentation, but the principles of pressing are the same for the production of red and white wines.

The quality of expressed juice is usually in inverse proportion to the degree of pressure used. The first juice extracted with the minimum of pressure is of good quality, although containing a higher proportion of polyphenols than free-run juice. This is often exactly what the winemaker needs to produce the correct balance in the final blend. It is only the later fractions pressed out with greater force that are of progressively lower quality, with the final fractions used only for vinegar production or for distillation. The greater the pressure, the more of the skin cells that are broken and the greater the concentration of the unpleasant, bitter tannins. Thus, the principle in good pressing is the use of minimum pressure to achieve the necessary extraction of juice.

5.6 Basket press

The earliest form of press is the **basket press,** otherwise known as the vertical screw press, which has remained virtually unchanged for over a thousand years. The mode of operation is simple, merely increasing the pressure on the mass of skins by screwing down the lid of the press, causing the cells to rupture and releasing their contents. The great drawback is that the process cannot be hurried. Increasing the pressure too rapidly results in a broken press. The problem lies in the physical nature of the solid mass, which is gelatinous and sticky, and out of which the juice can only exude slowly. To make things worse, the juice trickles out between the wooden slats of the basket, runs into a trough around the edge and from thence into a tub, all the time dissolving oxygen from the atmosphere. At the end of each pressing, the press has to be unwound, the skins cleared out with shovels and the press re-filled, all of which are labour intensive operations.

Despite these facts, the basket press is still used by some very high-class wineries in preference to more modern presses because the static bed of skins acts as a fine filter, yielding juice of good clarity. Most of the presses still used for champagne production are based on the basket press, using a basket that is shallow and of large diameter, to enable the juice to get away from the skins as quickly as possible, thus minimising the extraction of colour from the skins of the black grapes.

5.7 Vaslin press

The first stage in the evolution of the press was the **horizontal screw press**, typified by the Vaslin press, which is effectively a basket press turned through ninety degrees and given two pistons, one at each end of the slatted cylinder, with an access port on the side of the cylinder. The cylinder rotates on a horizontal axis about a stainless steel screw, on which are threaded the two pistons. The ingenious element of the design is that the screw is divided into two halves, one half being a right-handed thread, the other left-handed. The result is that if the screw is held stationary, when the press rotates, the two pistons move towards each other, the reverse rotation winding the pistons apart. Stainless chains are connected between the pistons, and as the chains straighten they break up the mass of skins after each pressing. Filling and emptying is simple, and the operation can be totally automated, even to the extent of automatic delivery of the juice from each pressing to separate vats, making it much more efficient in terms of time and labour.

5.8 Interior of Vaslin press

The complete sequence of operation is:

- With the door at the top, the press is filled and the door closed.

- The whole press is rotated, including the screw thread. This tumbles the grapes and releases the maximum free-run juice.

- While the rotation continues, a brake is applied to the screw thread to stop it rotating, which causes the pistons to move towards each other.

- Rotation continues, until the required pressure has been reached.

- The rotation is reversed, to part the pistons, the chains breaking up the mass of skins.

- Pressing is repeated several times, using a higher pressure each time.

- At the end of the operation, the door is opened and the press rotated until the door is at the bottom, when the skins fall out and the press can be re-filled for the next batch.

Its only shortcoming is that it produces a rather coarse juice, due to the high pressures that are required as the skins are progressively compressed into a smaller volume in the centre of the cylinder. This reduces the effective surface of the press to that portion between the two pistons.

The **pneumatic press** was developed by Willmes in order to overcome the problem inherent in the design of the horizontal screw press, so that a more efficient pressing could be achieved and at lower pressures.

5.9 Interior of a Willmes press

In this press, the two pistons are replaced by a cylindrical pneumatic bag, or bladder, or sausage, which can be inflated with compressed air (or even cold water, if cooling is required).

As the bag expands, the skins are pressed against the entire surface of the slatted cylinder, enabling the juice to exude under very low pressures, as low as 0.2 bar, resulting in superior quality.

The common fault with all of these presses is the danger of dissolving oxygen from the atmosphere, with the risk of destroying some of the more delicate constituents. The **tank press,** typified by Bücher, is a development of the pneumatic press, where everything takes place inside a closed tank, which can be pre-flushed with nitrogen and the juice pumped away without ever touching air. At present, this design is regarded as the ultimate by modern anaerobic winemakers because the combination of low pressures and gas flushing gives a high quality juice. Unfortunately, complex equipment is inherently expensive.

5.10 A tank press

All of the presses described above suffer from the same shortcoming: they are batch processes. They have to be loaded with grapes, operated to extract the juice and then emptied; a sequence which is tedious, time-consuming and labour intensive. Wineries handling very large quantities of grapes need presses that can work on a continuous principle, rather than the batch system of all other designs. Thus, the **continuous screw press** was developed, which achieved ill repute in its early days by virtue of the fact that it can squeeze grapes almost bone-dry, yielding foul juice fit only for brandy production.

5.11 A continuous screw press

Many winemakers reserve the use of the continuous press for the production of must which is intended for distillation into brandy, and in some countries, such as Algeria, its use is banned for the production of wine of controlled origin.

The original continuous press consisted of a strong steel tube, perforated along its length, containing an archimedes screw, which pushes the grapes through the pipe. Pressure is achieved by using a variable pitch screw, the turns coming closer together towards the outlet end of the press. The result is that the volume between each turn of the screw becomes steadily less as the grapes go through the machine. This generates huge pressures and produces juice of dubious quality. However, by a clever modification it is possible to take juice of a very acceptable standard from the low-pressure end of the press. The simple change to the design incorporates movable troughs underneath the press which catch juice escaping from the low-pressure end, further troughs diverting the higher-pressure juice to different vats.

Another version of the continuous press uses a simple archimedes screw of constant pitch, which turns to introduce grapes into a chamber at the far end of the screw. The whole screw then moves forward to press the skins against the end of the chamber. The screw then moves back, still turning, to introduce more skins, which are pressed on the next forward stroke of the screw. The advantage of this mechanism is that the pressure can easily be regulated by adjusting the forward action of the screw. Both of these modifications of the continuous press can be found in use in large modern wineries, where wine of good commercial standard is produced in large volumes.

Chapter 6

MUST ADJUSTMENTS

The real world is not easy to live in. It is rough; it is slippery. Without the most clear-eyed adjustments we fall and get crushed. A man must stay sober: not always, but most of the time.

Clarence Shepard Day 1874-1935

Grapes when crushed become must, from the Latin *mustum*, meaning the expressed juice of fruit. In winemaking the word is used rather loosely and can mean with or without the skins, before or during the fermentation. Only after the completion of fermentation does must become wine.

Throughout the winemaking world oenologists have been tempted to meddle with the natural balance of the must when the seasonal weather has been less than perfect. Despite the fact that it can be very frustrating at times, nature has a remarkable way of knowing what is best. Man has discovered that he can adjust what nature has produced, but only to a limited degree: the further we move away from the natural balance, the worse becomes the finished wine. Thus, in a poor year, when the normal acid-sugar balance is upset, small adjustments will yield an improvement, but larger changes make matters worse. Too much added acidity makes an 'angular' wine, and large volumes of added sugar merely dilute the natural fruit of the grape. It is quite logical, therefore, that wine producing countries have regulations that limit the adjustments that can be made to juice and wine, although these differ from country to country.

Another interesting principle that has been noticed from experience is that any adjustments that are felt necessary are best made to the must before fermentation, rather than to the finished wine. It would appear that the process of fermentation helps the adjustments to 'marry' more thoroughly, resulting in a wine that is more harmonious.

In order to administer the European regulations regarding aspects of grape production and wine making, Europe has been divided into wine growing zones that essentially follow the climatic differences across Europe. Zone A is the northernmost belt, covering England, Wales and most of Germany, zone B includes northern France and the southernmost part of Germany, while zone C gathers up the rest of Europe. As one has come to expect of modern bureaucracy, three simple zones did not suffice for the administration of complex regulations, so the zones have been sub- and sub-sub-divided! This enables the limitations on sugar and acid adjustment to be applied differently to quite small areas of Europe.

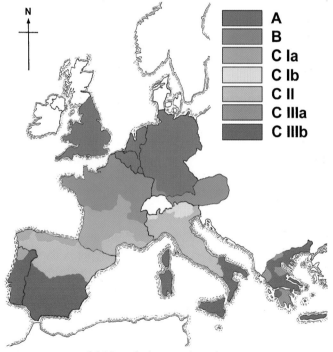

N

A
B
C Ia
C Ib
C II
C IIIa
C IIIb

6.1 Map of wine growing zones

The only changes to the natural balance that are allowed are the addition of sugar, and the addition or removal of acid, and only when specifically stated in the regulations, and within clearly specified limits.

45

Although adjustment of acidity is best done before fermentation, giving a more integrated wine, the regulations allow for this to be done both before and after fermentation, although the limitations on adjustment in the finished wine are tighter.

The must, at this stage, is in a precarious state, prone to attack by oxygen and by a host of different micro-organisms. It is a rich and nutritious medium and must be protected vigorously until the moment of fermentation. At this point all winemakers heave a sigh of relief because the active yeast and the copious evolution of carbon dioxide combine to give the must considerable protection. Until this moment, recourse is usually made to the protective action of sulphur dioxide.

Sulphur dioxide

Sulphur dioxide (SO_2) is the oldest and most versatile of all of the additives. It acts as an antioxidant, preventing oxidation by mopping up oxygen dissolved from the atmosphere. It also controls the growth of micro-organisms, killing bacteria and slowing down the development of the less desirable yeasts. Although probably added to the grapes before leaving the vineyard, by sprinkling with potassium metabisulphite, it is not until reaching the must stage that its concentration can be measured and the first of many adjustments made. (For more detail on sulphur dioxide, see p.124.)

In white wine production, the use of sulphur dioxide is universal during the clarification process (unless the hyperoxidation technique is being used, see p.27). It protects the must against oxidation, kills the bacteria that could degrade the must and stuns the wild yeasts, thereby giving the wine yeasts a chance to develop. It is possible to make wine without the use of sulphur dioxide, but extreme precautions have to be taken at all stages to prevent the ingress of oxygen because the wine will be very susceptible to oxidation. It is interesting to note that its use is permitted even in organic winemaking (more correctly, wine made from organically grown grapes).

In red wine production, sulphur dioxide is useful during maceration because, apart from its selective effect on the micro-organisms, it assists in the process of extracting the anthocyanins and other polyphenols from the skins. The only problem is that these compounds quickly combine with the sulphur dioxide, making it ineffective.

Clarification (white wines only)

Freshly pressed must contains considerable quantities of solid matter, mostly cellular debris from the skins, which can cause off-flavours in the wine, if not removed. Thus, clarification has become the norm in most wine producing areas of the world. However, the degree of clarification is very much part of the expertise of the winemaker. There is a danger in getting too enthusiastic about clarification, the solid particles being nutritious to yeasts because they have adsorbed on to their surface amino acids, minerals and vitamins. (Note that *ad*sorbed indicates a surface attraction, contrasting with *ab*sorbed, meaning distributed within the body of the solid, rather like a sponge.) The complete removal of these particles can reduce the nutritional value of the must to such a degree that the yeast has difficulty in starting a fermentation. It is a matter of knowing the grapes and the must, knowing how rich they are in nutrients, and knowing how much clarification is necessary.

In the traditional **settling** method (Fr. *débourbage*) the wine is left to stand for 12 to 24 hours, or even longer, during which time the particles sink to the bottom of the vat. This is a rather long period for must to be left in an unprotected state, but gravity is not a strong force and the particles are not very dense and fall somewhat slowly. The protection given by sulphur dioxide during this time is critical, because it not only acts as an antioxidant, but also reduces the activity of yeasts and bacteria. For the same reason, the must is often cooled to below 15°C, which slows down both the bacterial activity and any oxidation. At the same time, the cool wine will dissolve oxygen more readily, a factor which is favourable to the rapid start of fermentation (see page 56).

The period of clarification can be shortened considerably by **centrifuging**, which can separate the solids by centrifugal force in one to two hours. A centrifuge is an expensive machine that is based on a rotating conical drum that spins at very high speeds and can separate solids from liquids.

Centrifuging can be applied at any stage in winemaking where clarification is needed, e.g. before fermentation, after fermentation to remove yeast cells, or after fining to remove the deposit. However, some winemakers regard the centrifuge as a harsh tool that can cause damage to wine or must, so caution is necessary.

6.2 Centrifuges

One of the great dangers of using a centrifuge is that it can saturate the liquid with oxygen from the atmosphere, as the liquid is spinning in a thin film inside the cone. Although at the clarification stage this could be an advantage, at any other stage it is necessary to flush the interior of the centrifuge with nitrogen before use, to prevent the dissolution of oxygen.

Another process which is finding use for clarification is **flotation**, which has been used for decades in the mining industry for separating finely divided particles of ore from water. Small bubbles of nitrogen are blown up through the must, catching the solid particles and floating them to the surface, where they can be skimmed off. This can be adapted for the dual purpose of clarification and hyperoxidation at the same time by using air rather than nitrogen for the bubbling process.

Acidification

Grapes grown in hot climates, such as Australia or California, will possibly be lacking in acidity. This is easily rectified by adding acid, usually tartaric acid or malic acid, which are the natural acids of grapes. Tartaric acid is the chosen acid at this stage in vinification principally because it is the natural acid of ripe grapes, but also because it does not suffer from the problems that other acids might bring. Malic acid might well be broken down by the secondary fermentation (see below), resulting in an unwelcome loss of acidity. Citric acid, the acid of citrus fruits, is cheaper and readily available, but can be metabolised by some yeasts and converted into acetic acid, resulting in an increase in volatile acidity. In Europe, only tartaric and malic acids are allowed and indeed, acidification itself is only allowed in the hottest parts of Europe, zones Cii and Ciii.

The process of acidification is very simple; all that is involved is an initial tasting and analysis, followed by a calculation of the required amount of acid to be added. The acid is weighed out, dissolved in a little juice, added to the bulk and stirred.

Deacidification

In cool climates, which in reality prevail in the greater part of Europe, sunshine is usually in deficit, with the result that the acid level even in ripe grapes is on the high side. Hence, European regulations permit deacidification anywhere in Europe, with the exception of zone Ciii(b), which is the hottest zone and is usually desperate for more acid, not less!

Although chemically simple, the mechanism involved in taking acid out is not as straightforward as adding it, because acid cannot be physically removed, but has to be destroyed by a chemical reaction within the must itself. Furthermore, the acidity is not caused by a single acid, but is due to a mixture of acids, mostly tartaric acid and malic acid (see p.17).

The reduction in acidity, or deacidification, is achieved by the addition of a carbonate, such as calcium carbonate (chalk) or potassium bicarbonate, which neutralises the acids in the must. This is precisely the same reaction as the old-fashioned remedy for indigestion, when bicarbonate of soda is taken to reduce the acidity of the stomach.

The addition of chalk primarily removes tartaric acid, the product of the reaction being calcium tartrate, which comes out as calcium tartrate crystals. However, this causes great problems with tartrate deposits in the resultant wine because calcium tartrate forms crystals only very slowly, even with chilling, because its solubility remains much the same at all temperatures.

Some winemakers prefer to use potassium bicarbonate, as it does not involve the addition of calcium ions, thus avoiding the complications of the difficult removal of calcium tartrate. Potassium bi-tartrate crystallises easily because its solubility decreases considerably at low temperature.

A more recent practice is the use of what is known as double-salt deacidification, which uses specially prepared calcium carbonate containing a small proportion of finely powdered calcium tartrate-malate, a complex double salt. This is known by the brand name of Acidex and eliminates both tartaric and malic acids by forming crystals of calcium tartrate-malate, which is very insoluble. However, because of the expense, its use has been limited.

Due to the complication of the selective removal of the various acids, a technique sometimes adopted is to move a portion of the wine into a different vessel and then to add sufficient carbonate to totally neutralise all the acidity. The neutralised wine is then blended back into the bulk. This technique proportionately lowers the acidity due to all the acids, rather than that due to just tartaric or malic. The choice of method remains very much in the hands of the winemaker.

Enrichment

The practice of adding various forms of sweetening agents to must prior to fermentation appears to have started during the last quarter of the eighteenth century, although it was not realised at the time that the improvement in quality was due to an increased alcoholic content. It was not until 1815, at the end of the Napoleonic wars, that the addition of beet sugar became officially recognised. Jean-Antoine Chaptal, Comte de Chanteloup, once Minister of the Interior and Treasurer of the Senate, and a chemist by profession, suggested that the excess production of beet sugar could be used for enriching wine. Thus was born the practice still known as chaptalisation, a dubious memorial ill-befitting a man of great talent. Although the name of Chaptal is still associated with this process, it is gradually being dropped, particularly by the French, because of the ill repute that the misuse of this process has brought to French winemaking.

Enrichment has probably caused more controversy and more subterfuge than any other treatment. It is closely regulated in all European countries, according to the laws of each country. It is not allowed in Italy or Spain; in France its use varies from region to region, and, in Burgundy, from district to district.

Under cool conditions the natural sugar content of the grape is not sufficient to give an adequate level of alcohol in the finished wine. Under these circumstances, sugar is added to the must before fermentation, to boost the alcohol level in the finished wine. But what is an adequate alcohol level? Opinions differ widely. One fact is indisputable: the more sugar that is added to the must, the more the flavour is reduced, by the simple laws of dilution. On the other hand, if the alcohol is too low, the balance of the wine is affected. The correct level of enrichment is one of the critical decisions that have to be made by the winemaker.

European regulations allow the use of various forms of sugar at this stage. Chaptalisation has come to mean the use of beet sugar or cane sugar, both of which are composed of sucrose, the sugar used by M Chaptal. The other sugar, which is becoming more widely used, comes from the grape itself and is composed of concentrated unfermented grape juice. This is sometimes used in its crude form, but more often used after purification, when it is known as rectified concentrated grape must (RCGM). This is a colourless, syrupy liquid, with no smell or flavour, composed almost entirely of a solution of glucose and fructose, the natural sugars of the grape. When this form of sugar is used, the process has come to be known as enrichment, rather than chaptalisation. Officially, enrichment is either, and in practical terms there is no difference, because sucrose is always converted to glucose and fructose by the acids in the must before being fermented to alcohol. There is a considerable lobby to prohibit the use of sucrose for this purpose, the logical argument being that wine should be made entirely from the product of the grape. This would undoubtedly help to use some of the excess production of grapes throughout the world. However, the end result is identical, whether the sugars originate in grape, beet or cane: the debate is in the political arena.

One important fact should not be forgotten, and that is that enrichment has no effect on the sweetness of the finished wine. All the added sugar is fermented by the yeast and ends up as alcohol.

Other treatments

To counter any lack of natural nutrients, it is permissible to add a source of nitrogen in the form of ammonium phosphate or sulphites up to a total of 300 mg/litre. This nitrogen should not be confused with gaseous nitrogen (N_2), as used for blanketing wine to prevent the ingress of air to a vat. It is combined nitrogen, in the form of ammonium (NH_4) compounds, which are necessary for the formation of amino acids and proteins within the yeast cell.

Another nutrient additive is the vitamin thiamine, which is allowed at levels up to 600 mg/litre. Thiamine is an important vitamin in the growth of yeast populations.

Occasionally bentonite is added at the must stage to remove some of the proteins to reduce the viscosity of the must, but care has to be taken that the level of nutrients is not reduced too far. Another advantage of bentonite at this stage is that it will partially remove the polyphenoloxidase enzyme, one of the powerful oxidising enzymes, thus protecting the must from deterioration by oxidation.

If a must destined for the production of white wine is darkly coloured, it can be treated with activated charcoal, up to 100 g/litre, to reduce the colour. But care is needed, as charcoal removes flavour as well as colour!

Chapter 7

FERMENTATIONS

All love at first, like generous wine,
Ferments and frets until 'tis fine;

Samuel Butler 1692-1680

Fermentation processes are manifold, and before considering the transformation of grape juice into wine, it is necessary to define this process accurately, if palatable wine is to be the result. A biochemist would define a fermentation as any reaction involving either living micro-organisms or, at least, an enzyme extracted from such an organism.

Antibiotics, vitamins, monosodium glutamate, citric acid and acetone are all made on an industrial scale by fermentation processes. As wine makers and wine drinkers, we are interested in the alcoholic fermentation. This is a specific reaction during which yeasts feed on sugars and break them down with the aid of enzymes, producing alcohol and a considerable quantity of carbon dioxide gas and heat.

Wine is the fermented juice of the freshly gathered grape, or so runs the accepted definition. This short phrase enshrines a surprising number of sensitive principles:

- Wine cannot be produced without an alcoholic fermentation. Even non-alcoholic wines are initially made by fermentation, but are then subjected to processes that remove the alcohol (and much of the flavour!).

- Wine is made only from grapes. The products made from other fruits must be referred to as 'fruit wine', and must bear the name of the fruit on the label.

- The grapes must be freshly gathered (although the definition of 'fresh' is given a somewhat liberal interpretation in the making of Amarone, for example). The purpose of this clause is to exclude British wines and any other beverages made from grape concentrate.

But where and by whom was alcoholic fermentation discovered? Nobody knows; of that we can be certain. It was probably discovered by some inquisitive person who found a container of grapes that had been forgotten, or who discovered a hollow stone beneath a bees' nest and into which had dripped the honey, mixed with rain water. Natural fermentation would have occurred, yielding a strange-tasting liquid with miraculous powers!

Yeasts

Fermentation cannot occur without the presence of yeasts. Just as alcoholic fermentation is but one of a vast family of enzyme-related reactions, so the yeast used for alcoholic fermentation is a member of the huge family known as fungi, the same family that includes mushrooms and toadstools. Together with bacteria, they are responsible for the decay of all organic matter.

Yeasts are classified within fungi as *ascomycetes*, or sac fungi, fungi whose bodily form is that of a small sac or capsule. Most wine yeasts belong to the genus *Saccharomyces*, meaning sugar-loving, of which the species *cerevisiae* is the commonest. Different strains of this yeast are used for wine making, brewing and baking. In winemaking, other species are sometimes used, such as *Saccharomyces bayanus*, a yeast particularly associated with the flor in sherry production.

Yeast from other genera also appear in fermenting musts, especially those that are being fermented by the natural flora, and make up the group known as 'wild' yeasts. A commonly occurring member of this group is *Kloeckera apiculata*, a yeast with crescent-shaped cells, and intolerant of alcohol. Other species found in this group include *Saccharomycodes, Hansenula, Candida* and *Torulopsis.*

7.1 Cells of Saccharomyces cerevisiae

Much discussion and argument has taken place about the role of yeasts in the production of different flavours in the finished wine. Some maintain that the choice of yeast makes little difference, while other winemakers insist that the yeast selection is very important, especially in wine for drinking young. It is recognised that certain species are undesirable, such as *Brettanomyces* that can produce a mousy smell, so it does not seem unreasonable to assume that different species and different strains can produce different results, although these differences become smaller as the wine ages.

The action of yeasts

Yeasts are very adaptable organisms and can exist either aerobically, meaning in the presence of oxygen, or anaerobically, without it. In the aerobic state it reproduces rapidly, but does not produce any alcohol because its metabolism can extract all the energy from the sugars it is living on, producing water as an effluent. This is the ideal condition at the start of a fermentation because the population increases rapidly, preventing any deterioration in the must. Therefore, aeration of the must before fermentation is one of the few occasions where oxygen is actually welcomed.

If the yeast continued to have unlimited access to oxygen, no alcohol would be produced. But alcohol-free wine is not particularly attractive, as witness the several attempts at the creation of such products. So the yeast must be encouraged to switch to its anaerobic mode, in which it cannot metabolise the alcohol produced, and yields an alcoholic rather than an aqueous effluent. This change in behaviour occurs naturally because the dissolved oxygen in the must is quickly absorbed by the growing yeast population, soon resulting in anaerobic conditions.

The process of alcoholic fermentation can be summed up by the following:

> yeast + sugars → alcohol + carbon dioxide

This can be refined into a proper chemical equation, which can yield useful information:

$C_6H_{12}O_6$		$2C_2H_5OH$		$2CO_2$
glucose	→	ethanol	+	carbon dioxide
180		92		88

In this equation the grape sugars are shown as glucose, but in reality they are roughly equal quantities of glucose and fructose. These substances have the same empirical formula because the molecules are actually mirror images of each other, known as isomers. The predominant alcohol in wine is properly called ethanol, although there are smaller quantities of many other alcohols, all of which play a part in the ultimate bouquet and flavour. In simple terms, this equation shows that each molecule of sugar produces two molecules of alcohol and two molecules of carbon dioxide.

The figures under each substance are the relative quantities involved in the reaction, by weight, and are obtained from the molecular weights of the substances. The units can be anything, provided they are the same on both sides of the equation. Thus, from this equation, it can be deduced that 180 kg of sugar will produce 92 kg of alcohol and 88 kg of carbon dioxide, or approximating, a given weight of sugar yields roughly half its weight as alcohol and the other half is lost as gaseous carbon dioxide (CO_2). This is a huge amount of gas, a gas that is colourless, heavier than air, and is highly dangerous because it can fill empty vats and will cause immediate suffocation if breathed in high concentration. It is important that a good ventilation system is operational during fermentation, although in many older wineries this amounts to opening all the windows as wide as possible!

The figures in the above equation are all by weight, but alcoholic strength is always expressed by volume. To convert alcoholic units from weight to volume it is necessary to involve the density of alcohol in the calculations. Ethanol is less dense than water, weighing only 0.7897 grams per millilitre (water being approximately 1 g/ml). Using this fact, it can be calculated by simple mathematics that 17 grams of sugar per litre of must produces one percent of alcohol by volume. By using this formula in conjunction with the results of the sugar analysis, the winemaker can calculate how much sugar to add at the enrichment stage.

E.g. If a winemaker wants to make a wine at 12% vol alcohol and the analysis of the must shows it to contain 170 g/l of sugars. How much sugar must be added at the enrichment stage?

- It is known that 17 g of sugar per litre yields 1% vol of alcohol
- Therefore 170 g/litre will yield 10%vol
- The increase in alcohol required is 12 – 10 = 2% vol
- Therefore, quantity of sugar to be added is 2 x 17 = 34 g/litre
- For 4000 litres of must, total quantity of sugar to be added is 4000 x 34 = 136kg

Natural fermentation

In natural or traditional fermentation, use is made of the natural micro-flora that are found on the grapes, in the vineyard and on all the surfaces of the winery. This mixture of organisms consists of three basic groups: bacteria, wild yeasts and wine yeasts. In those parts of the world where wine has been made for centuries, the yeasts have gone through a process of mutation and natural selection, resulting in an adequate supply of good wine yeasts in the micro-floral blend.

At the beginning of the fermentation process most of the bacteria are knocked out by the sulphur dioxide which will have been added, and the wild yeasts, because they are more abundant than the wine yeasts, start the fermentation. At an alcohol concentration of around three per cent the wild yeasts start to die because they are intolerant of alcohol. The fermentation is completed by a mixed culture of wine yeasts that will vary from vineyard to vineyard and even from year to year. It is this unpredictable and somewhat erratic nature of natural fermentation that has resulted in the reduction of the number of wines produced by this ancient process. But there is a renewed interest in this subject, as it has been realised that the great and valuable attribute of natural fermentation is that it imparts character and individuality to the wine, due to the complex mixture of organisms that are present.

Cultured yeasts

Studies in wine research have shown that the nuances imparted by the yeast are quite considerable, although this effect is most marked in the earlier stages of maturity. Hence the interest in cultured yeasts, which offer the winemaker the choice of the characteristics of a particular yeast. The quality conscious winemaker selects yeast carefully, often after many years of experimentation.

Cultured, or selected, yeasts are cultures that have been taken from vineyards around the world, where wines have been produced for centuries and where there is a reasonable chance of finding top quality strains. It is a simple task for a microbiologist to separate individual colonies from a culture of mixed organisms and to grow each colony into a working population, which can be purchased either in a freeze-dried form or as an actively living culture on small slopes of agar, a nutritious jelly that will support live yeasts. The advantage of the freeze-dried form is that it has a longer shelf life and can easily be re-activated by mixing with fresh must.

Using a cultured yeast is simple, and does not necessitate the sterilisation of the entire vat of must because the success of one yeast over another depends on population density. The yeast with the greatest population wins (although it is possible to go still further and use what is called a 'killer' yeast, which produces toxins that destroy other yeast strains). Having purchased the culture, all that is necessary is to inoculate it into, say, 100 ml of must sterilised by filtration, put it in a warm place and allow it to grow until actively fermenting. This is then poured into a larger volume of must and left to develop. This in turn is added to the vat of juice, stirred and left to ferment. The actively developing added yeast overwhelms any other yeast that might be present in the must.

The disadvantage of using standard yeast strains is that the result is a standard wine, irrespective of the country of its production, always the same, always perfect. The great joy of the wines of the world is their infinite variety, and there can be no doubt that wines have moved closer together in style since the advent of modern winemaking.

The ultimate technique used by the more ingenious winemakers is to use a culture of yeast selected from the microflora of their own vineyard, by employing the services of a microbiologist to separate and culture each individual yeast. Trial fermentations are then carried out with the separate yeasts to discover which produces the best results. Thus, we get that valued combination of individuality with reliability of production.

Control of temperature

Yeast is a living organism and, like ourselves, produces heat when active and slows down when cold. A great deal of heat is produced during fermentation, which has to find an escape route. It is amazing to feel the heat radiating from a vat whose contents are in active fermentation – it is not surprising that cellar workers gather in this area during their tea breaks! Conversely, if the fermenting liquor becomes too cold, as can happen in chilly autumns in northern Europe, the fermentation will become too slow, or even come to standstill.

Temperature is an important factor during fermentation because there are two objectives that come into play, which depend upon opposing conditions. These are the extraction of flavour and colour components from the skins on the one hand, and the retention of volatile aromatic substances on the other. Warmth is required for the former, whereas for the latter, the cooler the better. For each wine there is an optimum temperature, balancing skin extraction with aroma. In the production of red wines, both of these objectives are important, and the choice of temperature is critical. Skin extraction, however, plays no part in the fermentation of white wines, because the skins are not present during the fermentation stage, the only consideration here being the retention of volatile aromas. Even if skin contact techniques have been employed, the skins are usually removed before fermentation commences. (See p.81) This is the basic reason that white wines are, in general, fermented at lower temperatures than red wines.

The control of temperature occurs naturally in a traditional cellar because the small size of the containers gives a high surface to volume ratio and thus an efficient mechanism for heat loss. Additionally, in northern Europe, the end of summer comes quickly, autumn is cold and the cellars become even colder, so there is usually little that needs to be done to remove the heat of fermentation.

When larger vats are used, or where the cellars are warm and dry, artificial cooling is necessary, because the surface area of large vats is insufficient to dissipate the large amount of heat produced. Vats such as these have cooling coils inside and jacketed walls, through which is circulated chilled brine or glycol solution, automatically controlled by thermostats.

The usual range for the fermentation of red wines is 20°C to 32°C, whereas whites are normally fermented at temperatures of between

10°C and 18°C. But, as with all winemaking activities, rules are frequently broken. Some red wines are fermented above 32°C and at least one brilliant producer of Muscat de Beaumes de Venise has persuaded his yeast to ferment at 0°C, despite all that has been written about yeasts not working below 5°C!

In recent years there has been a fashion for cold fermentation of white wines, because it has been realised that this technique gives an improvement on the dull beverages that used to be offered by the old-fashioned wineries, particularly in warmer climes. The result has been a proliferation of pale green wines tasting as if they were flavoured with essence of pineapple and banana. This flavour is produced by the retention of estery compounds that would normally be lost at higher temperatures and which impart a sameness to all of these products of low temperature fermentation. The ideal is to find the sensible balance between the warm conditions that result in the loss of aromatics, and the excessively low temperatures that produce the tropical fruit versions.

Controlling the fermentation

The rate of fermentation and the temperature of the fermenting liquid are inextricably linked: the higher the temperature, the faster the fermentation. The only means for controlling the rate of fermentation is by the control of temperature. In traditional small scale wineries nothing need be done, other than being prepared to take emergency measures should the ambient temperature become abnormally high or low.

In a modern winery, life should be even easier because temperature control can be automatic. It is very easy, with state-of-the-art equipment, to hold the temperature of even the largest vats to a remarkably constant degree. This does, of course, require the installation of high capacity cooling equipment. It is the lack of such capacity that often prevents the making of the highest quality wine in hot climates.

The progress of fermentation can be monitored simply by measuring the density of the fermenting liquid. Unfermented must is more dense than water, and alcohol is much less dense, so the transformation from must to wine is accompanied by a considerable drop in the density. By measuring the density regularly, it is possible to construct a graph of the progress of the fermentation. Adjustment of the temperature can then be used to control the rate of fermentation. The graph below shows the typical fluctuations that take place in a simple winery with basic cooling equipment. Years of experience have shown that, provided the temperature is maintained within a given range, these fluctuations are of no consequence.

7.2 The progress of a typical red fermentation

Stopping the fermentation

Fermentation comes naturally to a halt either when all the sugars have been exhausted, or when the yeast becomes poisoned by its own effluent, the alcohol. Alternatively, it may be due simply to a general weakening of the yeast, owing to a combination of sugar and alcohol, as in the production of the great sweet wines of the world, such as Sauternes or Tokaji Aszu. This natural termination of fermentation is the route followed by all winemakers of the old tradition – and the wine is essentially naturally stable. It will not re-ferment, does not require aseptic bottling and only needs protection from the atmosphere to prevent oxidation and the development of volatile acidity.

Although most fermentations are allowed to come to a natural conclusion, commonly known as fermentation to dryness, the intervention of science has provided several ways of terminating fermentation prematurely. These methods are of use when making wines of a particular style, such as port, or Asti Spumante, where halting fermentation before the end confers the particular characteristics of the wine.

1. Increasing the pressure of the carbon dioxide

During fermentation, much carbon dioxide is produced. If this is trapped above the wine by fermenting in a pressure vessel with the outlet valve closed, the pressure will rise. At about seven atmospheres the yeast will cease activity because it is effectively being suffocated by its own carbon dioxide. If the pressure is allowed to drop, the yeast will start the fermentation again. Therefore, increasing the pressure is only a temporary way of halting fermentation.

2. Reducing the temperature

Yeast activity, in common with most other forms of life, becomes slower as the temperature drops, until, at around 5°C, it ceases altogether – unless a super-cool yeast is present (see above). However, this is only a temporary measure, and if the temperature returns to normal, fermentation will re-commence.

3. Killing the yeasts

In the days of bad winemaking, when sulphur dioxide was splashed around in a carefree manner, some of the cheap desert wines were made by adding excessive amounts of this noxious chemical to kill the yeasts and arrest fermentation. With the stricter control of additives, this is no longer possible because the maximum sulphur dioxide allowed is much lower. A more acceptable way of killing yeasts is pasteurisation, the heat treatment widely used for killing micro-organisms in milk. In this process, the liquid being pasteurised is heated to about 95°C for one to two seconds, which destroys all the yeasts.

4. Removing the yeasts

A simple way of stopping fermentation is to remove the yeasts completely by filtration, or by using a centrifuge, which physically separates the solids from the liquid by centrifugal force. Once again, this is only a temporary effect: a few yeasts getting back into the wine will re-start the fermentation.

5. Adding alcohol, or fortification

Spirit can be added at an appropriate point during the fermentation, as in the production of port and vins doux naturels, to raise the alcohol level above that which the yeast can tolerate, and it dies.

Of all these methods of stopping fermentation, the only one that results in a stable wine is fortification. The product of all the other processes is unstable, in that fermentation can be re-established by the introduction of more yeast. To prevent re-fermentation in bottle, these wines have to be bottled aseptically, which means without troublesome micro-organisms.

A 'stuck' fermentation

The situation that all winemakers dread during the production of a normal dry wine, is when the fermentation stops unexpectedly, before all the fermentable sugars have been consumed. This can happen if there is a sudden drop in temperature, or if there is a lack of nutrients for the yeast, such as vitamins or amino acids. The problem in this case is persuading the yeast to come back to life, for it is frequently reluctant to do so. Merely warming the vat or barrel often has little effect. The only sure way of completing the fermentation is to gradually blend the 'stuck' must into another vat of must which is in active fermentation.

The malo-lactic fermentation : secondary fermentation

When the yeast fermentation, otherwise known as the alcoholic or primary fermentation, has come to an end, it is not the end of fermentations, because another one frequently takes place that involves a different set of micro-organisms.

Following on from the primary fermentation is the malo-lactic fermentation (M-L), also known as the secondary fermentation. (Note that this term has often been misused in relation to the faulty condition of wine fermenting in the bottle. This latter condition should be known as a second fermentation, or a re-fermentation, not secondary fermentation.)

The secondary fermentation used to be regarded as one of the great mysteries of winemaking. It had long been recognised that the character of the wine changed during the period following the end of the primary fermentation, becoming smoother and generally more pleasant. Unfortunately, because the mechanism was unknown, it was not possible to control the result. Although Pasteur, in the nineteenth century, discovered the action of micro-organisms, the mystery remained unsolved until the middle of the twentieth century, when Ribéreau-Gayon working with the wines of Bordeaux and Ferré in Burgundy discovered that the malo-lactic transformation was a fermentation involving a mixed culture of lactic acid bacteria.

We now know that the malo-lactic fermentation is the result of *lactobacillus* (and other micro-organisms) attacking the harsh tasting malic acid and transforming it into the softer tasting lactic acid. Once the mechanism had been established it became possible to control the result at will. The basic reaction is:

$$HOOC.CHOH.CH_2.\boxed{COO}H \rightarrow HOOC.CHOH.CH_3 + CO_2$$

malic acid　　　　　　　　lactic acid　　　carbon
　　　　　　　　　　　　　　　　　　　　　　dioxide

The carbon dioxide produced during the reaction disappears into the atmosphere unless the wine has already been bottled, in which case it renders the wine *pétillant*. This was the original source of the sparkle in vinhos verdes, although nowadays there are other, cheaper, ways of achieving the same result (pompe bicyclette!).

The softening of the acidity is advantageous in red wines, giving a smoothness and a suppleness which might have been absent prior to the action of the bacteria. Most winemakers ensure that all of their red wines have completed the malo-lactic fermentation before bottling, thus preventing the unpleasant taste of the active fermentation and the prickle of the dissolved gas developing in the bottle.

White wines that are intended to be full bodied and soft, such as many of those made from the chardonnay grape, are often encouraged to undergo the malo-lactic fermentation (provided they have sufficient initial acidity to prevent them from becoming 'flabby'). Those wines that are naturally crisp, such as products of Sauvignon Blanc, are usually preferred in their natural state. Sometimes in the case of a very acidic wine it is useful to enlist the aid of the secondary fermentation to reduce the acidity to an acceptable level. The paradox here is that in certain wines with very low pH, where the reduction in acidity would be most welcomed, the bacteria are reluctant to grow, as they are pH sensitive. In this case it is necessary to carry out a chemical deacidification in order to decrease the acidity to a level at which the organisms will grow.

The bacteria involved are quite varied, but all result in the destruction of malic acid and the production of lactic acid. They include various species and strains of *Lactobacillus, Leuconostoc* and *Pediococcus,* many of which are naturally present in the fermenting wine and will start spontaneously. However, if necessary, these can be purchased as cultures and are simply grown up in the winery and added to the wine, either during the primary fermentation or after it has finished. Being bacteria, they grow faster at higher temperatures and are readily killed by sulphur dioxide. Thus, the control of the secondary fermentation is simple: if it is wanted, the bacterial culture is added, the temperature of the wine is raised and sulphur dioxide is not added. Conversely, the prevention of the malo-lactic can be achieved by adding sulphur dioxide and keeping the wine cold.

The results of the M-L, to use its colloquial term, are generally looked upon with favour because not only does it reduce acidity, but it also increases complexity by generating additional flavour components such as diacetyl, the source of the buttery character. It also increases the stability of the wine by consuming bacterial nutrients. This is particularly useful in red wines, as they lack the protection of added sulphur dioxide, which becomes bound to the anthocyanins, the colouring pigments (see above).

However, there is sometimes a loss of fruit owing to a reduction in some of the fruity esters, which are broken down by the action of the bacteria. In addition, in some wines, the buttery flavour can be too dominant. It is fortuitous that control of the M-L is possible, although always with the risk that the fermentation will start at some time in the future, after the wine has been bottled. However, this is unlikely with modern techniques of aseptic bottling. (See p.178)

Chapter 8

VINIFICATION PROCESSES

Great fury, like great whisky, requires long fermentation.

Truman Capote 1924-84

Fermentation is but one part of the totality of operations that constitutes the making of wine. It is the expertise of the winemaker that governs the manner in which wine is made, and the choice of the processes used. These will vary according to the style of the wine being produced. At every stage, the winemaker can choose from a vast array of different techniques, and it is this choice that makes the difference between wine and great wine.

Red wines

The sequence of events in the making of red wine involves some or all of the following operations, in the order in which they are carried out:

- de-stemming
- crushing
- sulphiting
- adjustments to acid and sugar
- heat treatment
- fermentation
- maceration on the skins
- draining
- pressing
- clarification

The principal aim in the production of red wine is the extraction of colour and flavour from the skins, as the juice of virtually all black grapes is colourless. (There is one notable exception in the Alicante Bouschet, which has deeply coloured red juice and produces a black wine, which can be used to deepen the colour of anaemic wines).

This extraction is normally achieved by a combination of maceration and fermentation, although sometimes heat is also used to weaken the cell structure and release the polyphenols more readily.

When grapes are crushed, the yeast on the skins mixes with the juice and starts a fermentation, producing alcohol, which in turn extracts the polyphenols from the skins. This is a very effective and simple way of releasing the colour and flavour, but the major problem with this process is the production of large quantities of carbon dioxide, which are evolved as a myriad of small bubbles. These bubbles become entrapped in the solid matter, floating it to the surface. This is the process known as flotation, and is used at the clarification stage for the deliberate separation of solids and liquids. But at this point in the winemaking process the opposite is required and unless steps are taken to submerge this floating cap, trouble will quickly occur because the skins are swarming with acetic bacteria. In the warm and damp surroundings of the fermentation cellar this will soon turn the wine to vinegar. Furthermore, a floating cap of skins will not be in intimate contact with the liquid and will not be efficiently extracted by the liquid and therefore will not yield its full measure of flavour and colour.

8.1 The chapeau of skins

All the processes used for the making of red wine depend on the mixing of juice and skins. It is, however, important that this is carefully controlled to avoid over-extraction, which can result in a bitter, tannic wine, totally lacking in charm. The ideal situation is to allow the juice to percolate slowly through the skins, with minimum disturbance. The more the skins are agitated, the greater will be the extraction of the unpleasant fraction.

Traditional process

The earliest and the simplest method is to pump the mass of crushed grapes and juice into an open vat and to allow it to ferment naturally. When the evolution of carbon dioxide begins, the gas bubbles become trapped in the solids, which are raised to the surface. Here they form a compacted layer and eventually rise out of the liquid, forming a cap, known appropriately by the French word *chapeau*. This is a dangerous situation, with the combination of acetic bacteria, warmth and oxygen poised to convert the vat to vinegar overnight. So the cap has to be punched down manually several times each day (Fr. *pigeage*), which is a tedious and inefficient process and is really only suitable for small artisan wineries and for small volume fermentations of short duration.

The technique involves balancing on the edge of the vat, holding an unwieldy pole, on the end of which is attached a disk with which the floating layer of skins is punched down beneath the surface. In these days of health and safety awareness, it is somewhat surprising that this operation is still permitted, as a number of people have fallen into vats of fermenting wine whilst punching down the cap, several with fatal results. One might be tempted to comment "What a way to go!", but the loss of life is obviously not an occasion for joking, and, in any case, wine at this stage of its production is not a particularly pleasant beverage.

Submerged cap process

One approach to the problem of rising skins is to keep them submerged by placing a perforated screen just under the surface of the liquid. This prevents the skins from being pushed out of the liquid and eliminates the danger of the development of volatile acidity, but it is still an inefficient process because the skins become compressed under the screen, preventing efficient extraction. The relentless production of carbon dioxide compresses the skins ever more tightly against the screen, compacting them and preventing the gas escaping, until eventually something has to give. Indeed, vats have been known to burst, resulting in the total loss of the contents.

8.2 Fermentation with a submerged cap

An ingenious vertical stainless steel vat has been designed which overcomes this problem by incorporating a perforated riser pipe to permit the escape of gas from the body of the ferment. Being made of stainless steel, this design also incorporates automatic temperature control by means of cold brine circulating round the outside of the vat.

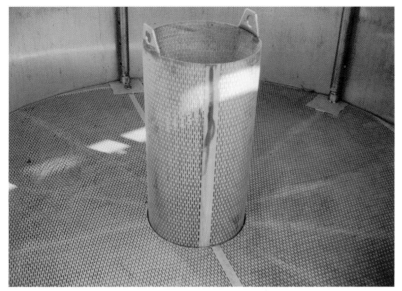

8.3 Modern submerged cap equipment

Pumping-over systems

An alternative approach to the mixing of skins and liquid is to pump the liquid from the bottom of the vat over the skins floating at the top. As the liquid percolates through the skins, an effective extraction takes place. In its simplest form this can be achieved in an old-fashioned concrete vat by fixing a spray head in the top hatch and pumping the juice from the bottom of the vat through the spray.

Large systems using the pumping over principle have been developed with specially designed vats, and are often used for making wines of medium to high quality. These vats are double the height of an ordinary vat, with a perforated screen that divides the vat into two parts. The crushed grapes are introduced into the upper part, from whence the juice drains into the lower section, where it ferments. A pump transfers the juice from the bottom section of the vat to the top of the vat, where it sprays over the skins and percolates down to the bottom section again, extracting the skins en route. As this takes place in a closed vat, there is no danger of dissolving atmospheric oxygen. Likewise, the mass of skins is not disturbed during the extraction process, the juice merely percolating through them, preventing over-extraction.

8.4 Vats designed for pumping over

Autovinificator (Autofermenter)

The Algerian Ducellier system, or autovinificator, is really another form of pumping-over, but is ingenious in that it needs no external power, harnessing the energy from the fermentation in the form of the carbon dioxide pressure to move the juice to the top of the vat. It was for this reason that it was developed in Algeria, where there was no electrical power in the distant areas of that vast country. The idea was transplanted to the Upper Douro for the same reason, although it is ironic that the Douro is now the source of vast amounts of electrical power from its hydroelectric schemes. Such is the efficiency and simplicity of the autofermenter that it can be found even in modern winemaking countries such as Australia.

8.5 Diagram of autofermenter

The autofermenter consists of a concrete vat in the form of a cube, with an open concrete trough on the top, fitted with a tube through which juice rises into the trough and a siphon through which it falls back into the main chamber. The crushed grapes are loaded into the chamber, which is then sealed. When the fermentation commences, the pressure of the trapped carbon dioxide causes the juice to rise through a tube into the trough at the top. When the level of liquid in the bottom chamber falls below the level of a gas escape tube, the pressure drops and the liquid in the trough cascades back into the lower chamber. As it does so, it thoroughly churns the skins and extracts the polyphenols in a very efficient manner.

8.6 Autofermenters dismantled

The original Ducellier tanks are still widely used both in Algeria for the production of good quality light wine, and in the Upper Douro where they are used for both port and light wine production.

Rotary fermenters

The rotary cement mixer has long been known for its simplistic and effective way of mixing solids and liquids. It was a short step to develop this principle for the mixing of grape skins and must. The blades inside the tank are designed in such a way that rotation in one direction results in a mixing of the contents; rotation in the opposite direction empties the drum. Its action is very effective because it achieves a thorough mixing of skins and juice and has found favour in the vinification of difficult grapes, such as pinot noir, whose thin skins contain a meagre level of colouring matter. However, this severe disturbance of the skins can lead to over-extraction, so expertise is vital in the operation of the rotary fermenter.

8.7 Rotary fermenters

Thermo-vinification

It is possible to extract the necessary components from skins by the use of heat, rather than the effect of fermentation. The method, as practised by eastern European countries in particular, is to heat the crushed mixture to 60 – 75°C, holding it at this temperature for 20 to 30 minutes and then to cool it down to fermentation temperature. This gives an intensely coloured must because the anthocyanins in the skins are readily extracted at elevated temperatures, owing to the weakening of the cell walls by the heat. This can result in a rather cooked flavour in the wine, unless care is taken to use only the minimum amount of heat.

A somewhat more sophisticated approach to the use of heat is to pass whole uncrushed grapes rapidly through a heat exchanger at 80°C, which heats only the surface layers of the grapes, the juice remaining cold. This releases the colouring matter and the aroma into the juice, without damaging the juice itself.

8.8 Must heating equipment

Carbonic maceration

Carbonic maceration is a widely used process, producing a wine that is ready for drinking in a matter of weeks rather than months or years. This makes it the accountants' dream, as it can have a very positive effect on cash flow. Financial considerations aside, it produces the style of wine that is popular, a wine that is of good purple colour, fresh and fruity on the nose, soft and eminently quaffable, and ready to drink.

The two important factors necessary to the success of this process are the use of whole bunches of undamaged grapes and a fermentation vessel that can be filled with carbon dioxide. The old name for carbon dioxide is carbonic acid gas, hence the name of carbonic maceration.

As can be seen from the picture opposite, any vat can be used for carbonic maceration, provided it can be closed at the top to prevent ingress of air. The fermentation usually takes place in two distinct stages, the first in a specially prepared closed vat at an elevated temperature, the second in an ordinary vat at normal temperature.

The main principle of carbonic maceration is that the first stage, the true carbonic maceration, takes place without the involvement of yeast. The alcohol that is produced during this phase is formed by intracellular fermentation inside the grape, using the grape's own enzymes, and it is for this reason that the grapes must be whole. During the second phase, the more usual extracellular fermentation takes place, using the yeasts from the skins of the grapes. In the past, this process has been misunderstood, so it is worth noting with care the main principles at each stage.

8.9 Carbonic maceration vats

The complete sequence of events is:

1. A vat that can be totally closed (usually a concrete vat with metal hatch covers) is flushed with carbon dioxide to sweep out all the air, thus eliminating all of the oxygen. It should be noted that the vat remains at atmospheric pressure throughout the process, but air cannot enter.

2. The vat is filled with whole bunches of undamaged grapes. It is important that the grape skin is intact, otherwise the juice will escape and an ordinary fermentation will commence.

3. Inside the vat, the grapes begin to die, owing to the lack of oxygen.

4. In common with all living organisms that are dying, the structure of the grape is attacked by the grape's own enzymes, which releases the sugars from within the cells.

5. The enzymes in the grape attack the sugars, breaking them down to alcohol. This is **intracellular** fermentation, and takes place in the absence of yeast (although it is the same biochemical process that occurs inside the yeast during normal fermentation).

6. This process is allowed to continue for between five and fifteen days at about 35°C, during which time about 3% alcohol is produced.

7. At the end of this period, the vat is drained, the juice separated, the skins pressed as usual and the press juice added to the free-run juice. Another unusual characteristic of carbonic maceration is that the press juice is of better quality than the free-run juice.

8. The combined juice is cooled to about 20°C, transferred to an ordinary vat and the fermentation allowed to run to completion, using the natural yeast from the grape skins (**extracellular** fermentation).

The result is a combination of the best of both worlds: good extraction of softened skins aided by the elevated temperature, followed by the completion of fermentation at a lower temperature, which retains the volatile aromas.

Probably the most famous wine produced by *macération carbonique* is Beaujolais Nouveau. It is ready to drink within two months of the fermentation, and should be consumed within six months, as it normally has a short shelf life. It is deficient in the tannins and polyphenols that confer longevity.

The other wines of the region, Beaujolais, Beaujolais Villages and the crus Beaujolais, are made by a method known as *semi macération carbonique*. In this method ordinary open topped vats are used and are not pre-flushed with carbon dioxide. The vats are filled with bunches of whole grapes, as with the true carbonic maceration technique.

Those at the bottom of the vat become crushed, the juice oozes out, coming into contact with the yeast on the skins and starts an ordinary extracellular fermentation. This produces a large volume of carbon dioxide, which, being heavier that air, gradually pushes the air out of the top of the vat, swathing the grapes in carbon dioxide, which promotes intracellular fermentation. These wines are thus the result of a combination of extra- and intra-cellular fermentation, of somewhat unknown proportions. It is the combination of these fermentation conditions with the fruit of the Gamay grape that gives Beaujolais its unique characteristics.

White wines

The production of white wines is relatively simple compared with the production of red wines because the must is separated from the skins before fermentation and thus there is no complication with floating solids. All the effort in making a good white wine goes into the preservation of the aromas by cool fermentation, and by the prevention of oxidation. In those instances where skin contact is practised (see p.34), the juice is usually separated from the skins before fermentation begins.

Although the techniques are similar to those used for red wine production, the order of operations is different:

- de-stemming
- crushing
- sulphiting
- skin contact
- draining
- pressing
- clarification
- adjustments to acid and sugar
- fermentation

Some of these processes have certain conditions that are of particular importance in the production of white wines.

Cool fermentation

The ready availability of refrigeration equipment for cooling and temperature control has encouraged winemakers to ferment white musts at lower and lower temperatures, but unfortunately, excessively low temperatures do not produce attractive wine. The results of such techniques are wines that are clinically clean, with aromas reminiscent of pineapple and banana, yet lack true varietal character and taste very similar, whatever their provenance.

It has been realised that there is an optimum temperature, which depends upon the grape variety and the style of the wine being produced, but will probably lie between 15°C and 20°C. The tendency now is to keep towards the higher end. At too low a temperature, too many of the volatile esters are retained, with the predominance of the estery pineapple aroma. As the temperature rises, so the true character of the grape is allowed to show itself. At high temperatures the volatile components are lost, and the wine becomes dull and lifeless.

Barrel fermentation

There has been an upsurge in barrel fermentation of white wines in recent years because it has been realised that better integration of oak flavours can be achieved by fermenting in the barrel, as opposed to merely ageing in the wood. The choice of barrel size is important in relation to fermentation temperature. Smaller barrels have a greater surface to volume ratio than larger barrels and, hence, are more efficient at dissipating the heat of fermentation. This is the reason why the traditional size of 225 litres was adopted in Bordeaux, being appropriate to fermentation in a cool cellar. Refrigeration is rarely needed, warming being more usual to prevent a fermentation stopping prematurely, where wines are still fermenting in the late autumn in a particularly cold season.

8.10 Tumultuous fermentation

A second advantage of barrels over vats is that an ample supply of oxygen is available for the first stage of fermentation, enabling the yeast to reproduce more rapidly because it is in its aerobic phase. This gives a quick start to the fermentation, and usually results in a higher alcohol in the finished wine.

The reactions going on in the barrel during fermentation are quite complex and have a major effect on the structure of the finished wine. The presence of yeast inside the barrel changes the interaction between wine and wood, and plays an active role in the balance between fruit flavours and wood flavours. In the first instance, the yeast cells coat the inside of the barrel, which reduces contact between wine and wood, and secondly, the yeast can absorb some of the wood extracts, changing them by a biochemical transformation into less aromatic compounds. The overall result is a more subtle and harmonious blend. Furthermore, the mass of yeast cells acts in a similar way to the polyphenols in red wine, protecting the wine from oxidation.

At the end of the fermentation there is the choice between racking the wine off the sediment or leaving the wine on the lees. In the latter case, it is important that the lees are stirred periodically

(Fr. *bâtonnage*), to prevent the risk of reductive flavours developing within the sediment. The mass of yeast cells has several further useful properties. As the yeasts die they release valuable substances known as polysaccharides, which act as natural fining agents, reducing bitterness from the wood tannins and thereby softening the wood flavours. They also increase complexity, improve the clarity of the wine, and prevent oxidation and an increase in colour.

The selection of the provenance of the oak and the degree of toasting enables the winemaker to control the flavour of the finished wine, although this aspect of the influence of oak belongs more to the maturation phase because the effect is more pronounced in the absence of yeast cells.

The disadvantages of barrel fermentation relate to the cost of barrels, the difficulty of hygiene and the large amount of manpower involved in the handling of these comparatively small units. There is also a loss of freshness and of fruit, and an acceleration of maturity. So this mode of fermentation is only used for those white wines which have sufficient body and structure, and are valued for their richness and complexity, and is not suitable for young fruity wines for early drinking.

Prevention of oxidation

One of the modern principles of the making of white wine is the prevention of oxidation, for oxygen is the great destroyer of fruit. Red wines are less susceptible to oxidation, containing high levels of polyphenols, which act as natural antioxidants. White wines do not have this protection. The old style white wines from Spain, France, Italy and eastern Europe were dreadfully dull, brownish in colour, with a nose of wet cardboard and a palate tasting of anything but fruit, all rounded off with a finish of sulphur dioxide. This was mostly the result of poor oxygen control.

One of the revolutions in modern winemaking has been the production of pale coloured, delicately fruity white wines, refreshing and eminently drinkable. Much of this style is the result of the elimination of oxygen at every stage in the winemaking process:

- Pressing the grapes in a tank press, pre-flushed with nitrogen

- Moving the juice through pipework and into vats where all the air has been removed by flushing with carbon dioxide or nitrogen

- Checking all joints for integrity of seals, especially pump seals

- Never keeping wine in a part-filled tank, unless blanketed with nitrogen

- The correct use of antioxidants, especially sulphur dioxide and ascorbic acid

- Attention paid at all times to keeping dissolved oxygen at low levels

Chapter 9

PRINCIPAL COMPONENTS OF WINE

One barrel of wine can work more miracles than a church full of saints.

Italian proverb

The style and balance of each individual wine is dependant on the relative abundance of constituents originating from two different sources. The first group can be found in the original grape juice and the others arise as a result of the fermentation process. The grape juice supplies the sugars, the acids, the minerals and nutrients, the polyphenols which embrace the tannins for 'grip' and anthocyanins for colour, and the crucial flavouring substances.

The fermentation creates other components that differentiate wine from mere grape juice. These include the alcohols, an expanded range of acids, glycerol and all the products of inter-reaction between these constituents.

Alcohols

During the process of fermentation yeasts produce alcohols, of which there are many different types. The predominant alcohol, by a considerable margin, is ethyl alcohol, or ethanol. This is the substance that has become abbreviated to 'alcohol' in all references to alcoholic beverages, conferring upon them their well-known characteristics: a warmth in the throat, a feeling of elation, then depression and ultimately drunkenness.

All alcohols have molecules that are constructed of chains of carbon atoms (C) with hydrogen atoms (H) attached, ending in the group that gives alcohols their special characteristics, the –OH group. The different alcohols simply have different lengths of the carbon chain.

CH_3OH	CH_3CH_2OH	$CH_3CH_2CH_2OH$	$CH_3CH_2CH_2CH_2OH$
methanol	ethanol	propanol	butanol

The first in the series, with only one carbon atom is known as methyl alcohol, or methanol. This is a particularly unpleasant alcohol whose first effect is to make one feel very ill, followed by blindness, madness and then death. All wines contain some methanol, but in very tiny proportions. It is only a serious threat to health in badly conducted distillations: hence the tight control on illicit spirits in many parts of the world. Being a smaller molecule than ethanol, it boils at a lower temperature and distils first, as part of the 'heads' and can thus be discarded.

There are many other alcohols produced during fermentation, all of which have bigger molecules than ethanol. These are not as toxic as methanol, but are still unpleasant in anything but trace quantities, resulting in headaches and nausea. As a group they are known as the higher alcohols or fusel oils. Because they have a higher boiling point than ethanol, they remain behind in the still at the end of distillation, where they are a component of the 'tails'.

All of these alcohols have an important part to play in the maturation process of the wine. During this period they react with the natural acids to form the heady fruity substances known as esters. The familiar aromas of pineapples, bananas, strawberries, raspberries and most other fruits are due to the natural esters in the juice. Fresh grape juice does not contain many of these esters, but they are formed as a combined result of fermentation and maturation, hence the presence of the aromas of various fruits in the bouquet of a mature wine. Some of the higher alcohols have a powerful aromatic aroma of their own and contribute directly to the character of the wine. So it is not unreasonable, as some would suggest it is, to describe the characteristics of a wine in terms of other fruits and of flowers: the probability is that the same chemical compound is responsible in both cases.

Musts with high levels of sugar yield wines with a high concentration of alcohol, unless steps are taken to halt the fermentation prematurely, which can happen naturally if the yeast is weakened initially by a very sweet must. High alcoholic strength is usually not the prime objective of any winemaker, as alcohol, *per se*, does not confer quality, although in hot climates it is difficult to avoid elevated levels. Although it is not possible to lower the strength, except by blending with a wine of lower alcohol, the alcoholic strength can be raised by a limited amount (controlled by regulations) by the addition of sugar prior to fermentation (see p.51).

Acids

Acids play a very important part in the constitution of wine. Without them, the colours would be strange, the flavour bland and the keeping qualities greatly reduced. Although tartaric and malic acids are the principle source of acidity, arising from the grape itself, during fermentation many more acids are produced as a result of the biochemical action of the yeasts. Two acids always present as a direct result of fermentation are lactic acid and succinic acid. A second source of lactic acid is the malo-lactic fermentation, where bacteria convert malic acid to lactic acid. Other acids variously produced are propionic, pyruvic, glycolic, fumaric, galacturonic, mucic, oxalic and more.

This complex array of acids has an important role in their reaction with alcohols, leading to the formation of esters *(see above under Alcohols)*.

The chemical structure of the different acids is more varied than alcohols and is more difficult to comprehend, but the one thing they all have in common is the acid group – COOH that confers on the molecule the acid properties. The so-called total acidity of the wine is due to the sum of all the acid compounds.

Control of total acidity is achieved principally at the must stage because experience shows that adjustments are best made before fermentation, since it would appear that the process of fermentation helps to blend the adjustments in some way. However, it is permissible to make further adjustments of acidity in either direction after fermentation. In all cases, a laboratory analysis of total acidity is advisable in order to calculate the correct addition of acid (see p.147).

Volatile acidity (VA)

Volatile acidity is a misused term, and should not be regarded as derogatory. Volatile acidity is that acidity which is due primarily to acetic acid, the acid of vinegar. All wines contain a certain amount of acetic acid, a natural component of their constitution, which adds to their complexity. It is only a fault when in excess, which can be prevented by good housekeeping.

Acetic acid is produced by the oxidation of alcohol, particularly under the influence of acetic bacteria (acetobacter).

$$CH_3CH_2OH \; + \; O_2 \; \rightarrow \; CH_3COOH \; + \; H_2O$$

$$\text{ethanol} \qquad \text{oxygen} \quad \text{acetic acid} \qquad \text{water}$$

These bacteria are aerobic, needing oxygen to do their dirty work. Hence, quality control in this area is simple: the wine should be kept free from bacteria and away from oxygen. Unfortunately, grapes are swarming with acetobacter and the atmosphere is 20% oxygen, so distinct action has to be taken to avoid trouble. A well-equipped modern winery has efficient filtration equipment for removing bacteria and a gas-blanketing installation (using nitrogen or carbon dioxide, or a mixture of both) for sweeping out air from vats and pipelines. Sulphur dioxide controls the acetobacter because they are very sensitive to it and are soon calmed down by a judicious dose at the right moment.

Wines suffering from excess VA do not usually smell of vinegar, but of nail varnish remover or cellulose thinners, which consist of commercial ethyl acetate. The reaction is identical to that which helps to form the bouquet during maturation in bottle; it is the process known as esterification, when acids react with alcohols to form esters, which all have powerful volatile aromas.

$$CH_3CO\,OH \; + \; H\,OCH_2CH_3 \; \rightarrow \; CH_3COOCH_2CH_3 \; + \; H_2O$$

$$\text{acetic acid} \qquad \text{ethanol} \qquad \text{ethyl acetate} \qquad \text{water}$$

The EU limit for red wine is 1.2 g/litre expressed as acetic acid, which, for most wines does not present a problem because VA becomes noticeable at levels around 0.8 g/litre. Difficulties in complying with the regulations occur only in older wines, where the VA can rise with time, and with wines from hot climates, such as the eastern Mediterranean and North Africa, where the natural VA is higher, due to the increased rate of activity of bacteria with the higher temperatures.

White and rosé wines very rarely exhibit excess volatile acidity, principally because the grape skins, which are the prime source of the bacteria, are removed early in the process of winemaking. The EU limit for these wines is accordingly set at the lower level of 1.08 g/litre as acetic acid, although this seems to be very generous for wines that have 0.4 to 0.5 g/litre as a normal level.

Residual sugars

Residual sugars is the name given to the residue of sugars that is left when a fermentation has come to an end. The trio of alcohol, acidity and residual sugars forms the balance of all wines. At the natural end of fermentation, when most of the sugars have been consumed by the yeast, a dry wine will result with around two to three grams per litre of residual sugars. Many branded wines intended for everyday consumption are made to a standard specification by blending a dry wine with a measured quantity of unfermented grape juice. This can be either as *süssreserve* (preserved grape juice) or rectified concentrated grape must, which is grape juice that has been concentrated and purified. Ordinary cane or beet sugar, which is sucrose, is not allowed for the purpose of sweetening finished still wine: it is allowed only for enriching grape must before fermentation and for sweetening sparkling wine. By this method of adding a sweetener, it is possible to create dry, medium and sweet wines from the same base wine.

The sugars are present mainly as the natural grape sugars, glucose and fructose. If a sparkling wine has been sweetened with sucrose, none of this will be present by the time the bottle reaches the table. All of the sucrose will have been changed by the acids in the wine to a mixture of equal parts of glucose and fructose, a process known as inversion. When a must has been enriched with sucrose before fermentation, the sucrose is converted first to a mixture of glucose and fructose by the process of inversion, and then finally to alcohol by the action of the yeast. Technically, it makes no difference whether a must or a wine has been sweetened by grape sugars or by sucrose: it is purely a matter of controlling legislation.

The EU, with its propensity for regulation, has introduced legal definitions of the various descriptions of sweetness and dryness. The basic limits for sugar for each category are easy to understand, but the augmented limits for increased acidity levels are complex and somewhat bureaucratic, even if they do recognise the relationship between sugar and acidity.

- Dry wines – Up to 4 g/litre of sugar, or up to 9 g/litre where the level of total acidity expressed as tartaric acid does not fall more than 2 g/litre below the final residual sugar content.

- Medium Dry – Up to 12 g/litre, or up to 18 g/litre where the total acidity is not more than 10 g/litre less than the final residual sugar content.

- Medium or Medium Sweet – Exceeds the level for Medium Dry, but does not exceed 45 g/litre.

- Sweet – Not less than 45 g/litre.

Yeasts will normally carry on fermenting a must until all the sugars have been consumed, so it might be wondered how the great sweet wines of the world can be produced without stopping the fermentation artificially. In fact, the fermentation stops naturally by virtue of the very high sugar level in the original must. Excess sugar is just as toxic to yeast as is the alcohol that it is producing, by virtue of the phenomenon of osmotic pressure. This is the principle by which nature tries to even things out. If two solutions are separated by a thin membrane, such as a cell wall, water tries to move across the membrane from the weaker solution to the one of higher strength, thus making them equal. Therefore, if a yeast finds itself in a strong sugar solution, its cells become dehydrated as its own water tries to dilute the sugar solution. Hence, the yeast is weakened and it dies before completing the fermentation.

By way of a footnote, residual sugars are sometimes referred to as reducing sugars. This is because most of the residual sugars are glucose and fructose, which have reducing properties and will react with a chemical known as Fehling's Solution. (See p.151)

Glycerol

Glycerol, or glycerine, is a major by-product of fermentation and is frequently the next most abundant constituent of wine after water and alcohol. Originating from the sugar in the grape juice, it is not surprising that the higher the sugar content of the must, the higher the concentration of glycerol, although this can be affected by the yeast strain used. Thus, wines from hotter regions generally have higher concentrations than those from cool climates.

In its natural, pure state it is a colourless, viscous liquid, with a slightly sweet taste. It plays a considerable role in the mouth feel of wine, imparting a smoothness and weight, without giving it overt sweetness. The 'legs' that appear round the edges of wine in a glass are due to the surface tension effect of a combination of glycerol and alcohol. It is not surprising, therefore, that heavy-weight wines from the hotter parts of the globe show the most pronounced legs in the glass.

Grapes that have been affected by botrytis cinerea already contain glycerol as a result of metabolism of the grape sugars by the noble rot. The additional glycerol produced during the subsequent fermentation gives botrytised wines their supremely smooth viscosity, and can reach levels as high as 30 grams per litre.

Chapter 10

CLARIFICATION AND STABILISATION

Wine is considered with good reason as the most healthful and the most hygienic of all beverages.

Louis Pasteur 1822-95

Is treatment necessary?

A new wine fresh from the fermentation is not a pleasant beverage; it is cloudy with yeast cells, has a dank nose of decomposition and can cause severe bowel problems if drunk in quantity. Yet, beneath this dark blanket lies the embryo of a lovely, pleasurable and health-giving drink. All that is necessary is a gradual stripping away of the substances that are covering up the true nature of the wine. Much of this would occur naturally, given adequate time, but careful intervention, expertly applied, can shorten this period.

Wine is a complex mixture of natural substances, many of which are in a constant state of change. Despite modern analysis and the application of treatments both ancient and modern, wine in bottle sometimes contains solid matter, either in suspension or sitting on the bottom of the bottle. The deposits could be either proteins or tartrate crystals, both of which are natural wine components, or they could be the result of reactions between the various minerals in the wine, or between the proteins and the tannins. Of one thing we can be certain, that the deposits are harmless because harmful organisms cannot thrive in wine, owing to the presence of alcohol and acids.

Whereas knowledgeable wine drinkers happily accept, and even expect, deposits in bottles of fine wine, the vast majority of consumers, who drink simple wine regularly, expect the wine to be star bright to the last drop. In a way this is a pity, because virtually every treatment to which wine is subjected removes a tiny portion of the quality (with the possible exception of certain fining agents).

The principle of good winemaking should be minimum treatment and minimum interference, a principle, which is known as 'low intervention' winemaking. Nevertheless, to satisfy the requirements of the majority, there are treatments and additives available to reduce the probability of deposits. These treatments are intended to produce a stable product, which will remain clear in the bottle and which will enable the consumer to drain it to the last drop.

Racking

Once the bubbles of carbon dioxide have stopped rising, indicating that the fermentation has been completed, the first natural clarification takes place, due simply to gravity. The dead yeast cells and cellular matter from the grape fall to the bottom of the fermentation vessel, forming what is known as 'the gross lees', meaning the initial large deposit. This deposit must not be left in contact with the wine because it will decompose, imparting to the wine an unpleasant, bitter taste, a condition known as 'yeast bitten'.

As soon as the wine has shown signs of becoming clear, which usually takes one to two days in a large tank, the wine is carefully drawn off, leaving the solid deposit in the bottom. This operation is known by the curious wine industry term of 'racking', which appears to be derived from the old English word 'rakken', meaning the skins, pips and stalks of grapes.

In a large modern winery, this process is too slow, so use is made of the centrifuge to clarify the wine, in the same way that it would have been used to clarify the must prior to fermentation. The principle difference in use after fermentation is the danger of dissolving oxygen from the atmosphere, so it is essential that the interior of the centrifuge be flushed with nitrogen before use.

Protection from oxidation

When the fermentation has finished, the wine loses the protection of the carbon dioxide that has been evolving throughout the fermentation, and becomes prone to oxidation, a condition from which it will suffer for the rest of its life. The good winemaker is well aware of this and will take steps to ensure that all the necessary controls are in place.

Additionally, one of the consequences of the production of carbon dioxide during the fermentation is that all of the free sulphur dioxide will have been lost. It will have been swept out of the wine by the action of the bubbles. It is necessary therefore to add a fresh dose of sulphur dioxide at the end of fermentation, before any damage can be done.

Dissolved oxygen

Oxygen possesses a dual nature: in the right place at the right time, it aids the development of wine, but when allowed unlimited access, it can lead to its destruction. Oxygen dissolves readily in water, as anyone knows who keeps fish. Since wine is at least 85% water, it is not surprising that oxygen will dissolve in wine if it is allowed contact with air. Now, every atom of oxygen that dissolves in wine destroys four times its weight of sulphur dioxide, as shown by their relative molecular weights:

$$SO_2 + [O] \rightarrow SO_3$$
$$64 16$$

Dissolved oxygen, often abbreviated to dO_2, is eventually destroyed by the sulphur dioxide, but this does not happen immediately, research having shown that dissolved oxygen and sulphur dioxide can coexist in wine before inter-reaction takes place. During this time every molecule of dissolved oxygen is a threat to the quality of the wine, taking it another small step towards destruction. The only secure way of preventing oxidation is by preventing air from coming into contact with the wine by the use of inert gases and by keeping vats brim-full and sealed.

Inert gases

In anaerobic winemaking much use is made of what are known as inert gases. In fact, this is a misuse of the word 'inert', which means 'deficient in active properties'. To a chemist, the inert gases, otherwise known as the noble gases, include helium, neon, argon, krypton and xenon, and are truly unreactive and require extreme conditions to make them react with any other substance. (Because of its low density compared with the normal atmosphere, a lung-full of helium gas alters the voice to a strange high-pitched squeak!)

The inert gases used by the winemaker are usually nitrogen and carbon dioxide. In this context the word 'inert' is used to mean something nearer to 'harmless', or specifically something that can be used to prevent air from coming into contact with the wine.

Carbon dioxide is popular because it is cheap and easy to use, being heavier than air. If applied gently at the bottom of a tank, it will push the air out of the top. This is an efficient way of removing the oxygen from a tank before filling with wine or must. A simple technique often used to achieve this is to add some blocks of 'dry ice' (frozen carbon dioxide) to a small quantity of wine in the bottom of the vat. The wine warms the dry ice, which causes a rapid evolution of carbon dioxide gas, pushing the air out of the top of the vat.

However, carbon dioxide does have drawbacks. Firstly, it dissolves in wine; the colder the wine, the more it dissolves. Not only does the oxygen barrier disappear, but also the wine gains an unpleasant 'prickle' on the palate. Worse than this, in human terms, is that it is invisible and very dangerous. At a proportion of only five per cent in the atmosphere it can cause unconsciousness and death. Being invisible and heavier than air, many people have died by going down into apparently empty vats to clean them, only to find that they are overcome by carbon dioxide. Death from asphyxiation is rapid, and to an observer outside the vat, the cause of death is not obvious. In the UK, as in many other countries, the laws on entering enclosed spaces are strict: an empty vat should never be entered until the atmosphere inside has been tested and found to be safe, and a second person must always be present outside the vat in case of emergency.

Nitrogen is the alternative inert gas and has quite different properties from carbon dioxide, the principal one being that it is roughly the same density as air. This is a disadvantage when flushing out tanks, requiring at least three times the volume of the tank to achieve an adequate removal of oxygen. On the other hand, it is almost insoluble in wine, so does not disappear by dissolving in the wine, and it is much less toxic than carbon dioxide. Being the same density as air, it does not collect in low-lying places and disperses readily. After all, the atmosphere in which we live is about eighty percent nitrogen.

An efficient sequence for oxygen control using inert gases would be:

- Flush out the empty tank with carbon dioxide.

- Fill the tank to the brim with wine, using nitrogen pressure to move the wine through the pipes.

- As the wine is removed from the tank, allow nitrogen to fill the headspace, preventing the ingress of air.

Sparging is the ultimate refinement in the use of inert gases. This is the process of injecting fine bubbles of gas into a liquid. As the bubbles pass through the liquid, a complex interchange takes place between volatile elements in the liquid and in the gas. If nitrogen is used as the sparging gas, any oxygen dissolved in the wine passes into the nitrogen bubbles and is thereby removed.

Small amounts of carbon dioxide dissolved in wine are important, giving the wine freshness and liveliness. Conversely, too much dissolved carbon dioxide is undesirable, especially in red wines, where one expects smoothness and softness. Mixtures of carbon dioxide and nitrogen of varying proportions can be used during the sparging process to control this. A high proportion of carbon dioxide in the sparging gas will increase the level in the wine; a low concentration will reduce it.

Blending

After the first racking, although the wine is in a somewhat raw condition, an experienced winemaker can get some idea of the quality of the finished wine. It is at this stage that the first round of tasting occurs, with a view to the ultimate blend that will make up the final wine.

To many people, both those in the wine trade and those who simply enjoy wine, blending is often regarded as a somewhat dubious operation, a means of getting rid of second rate wines. This is a false image of what is a very important aspect of wine production. Blending ranks with fermentation as a critical part of the winemaking process. Virtually all wines produced anywhere in the world are blended before being bottled. The 'grand vin' of a classed growth Bordeaux château, for example, will be blended from the best vines, the best parcels of the vineyard, the best barrels etc. Sometimes the addition of as little as five per cent of another permitted variety is added, and can have a major effect on the style of the wine.

The production of a medium price branded wine involves an incredibly complex blending operation, with components from many different sources:

- different grape varieties
- juice from different pressings
- fermentation at different temperatures
- fermentation with different yeasts
- fermentation in wood
- storage in stainless steel
- maturation in oak

By this means, the winemaker can control the style of the finished wine to a very close degree, and can even make several different wines from the stock of bulk wine at his disposal.

It is important that the blend is created before the clarification and stabilisation treatments take place because the blending of different wines can upset the balance that has been created by the various processes, rendering the wine unstable again.

Fining

Fining is an ancient process of clarification that is universally used for two purposes, for the prevention of haze and for the removal of some of the tannins to improve the balance of the wine. The original substances used for this purpose were mostly of animal origin, such as milk, egg whites and even the blood of oxen, although this latter fining agent has not been permitted in Europe since the introduction of the wine making regulations in 1987. The active components of all of these agents are naturally occurring proteins, available nowadays in purified form, such as casein from milk, and albumin from egg whites and other animal sources. In 1997, in response to concern about the spread of bovine spongiform encephalopathy (BSE or 'mad cow' disease), the French forbade the use of albumin prepared from cows' blood. Modern winemakers find the pure substances more reliable and easier to use.

Fining is a process which removes colloids from the wine by the addition of another colloid. But what are colloids?

Freshly made wine contains three main groups of substances:

1. The simple molecules, such as alcohols, acids and sugars. These substances form solutions in the wine, are a necessary part of its structure and remain in it through all the treatments.

2. The large particles, such as pieces of grape cell, yeasts, and other substances, all of which contribute to the cloudiness of the wine. These substances can all be removed by the straightforward process of filtration.

3. Substances with large molecules, but not sufficiently large to render themselves visible by causing cloudiness. They are also not large enough to be removed by a filter. These constitute the group of substances known as colloids.

Colloids themselves can be divided into two types, the stable and the unstable colloids. The stable colloids cause no problems, being invisible in solution and remaining so. In fact, one of the stable colloids, gum arabic, the same substance that used to be used for gumming paper and known as Gloy, is sometimes added to wine to increase its stability. It is the unstable colloids that have to be removed, because they will make the wine cloudy after bottling.

The molecules of these unstable colloids carry an electrostatic charge when youthful, the same charge for each molecule. Molecules with the same electrostatic charge repel each other, which keeps them apart and renders them invisible in solution. With age, when the protein denatures, the molecules rearrange themselves and lose the electrostatic charge, which enables them to clump together and form solid matter. Although totally harmless and tasteless, these colloids have to be removed if the wine is to remain clear and bright.

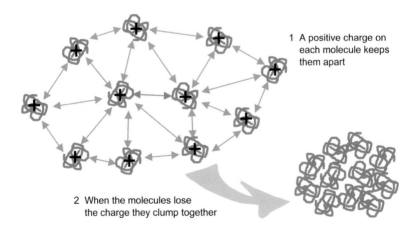

1 A positive charge on each molecule keeps them apart

2 When the molecules lose the charge they clump together

10.1 The behaviour of unstable colloids

The process of fining is very simple, which is why it is so widely used and has been for generations. In essence, it achieves the same result as would occur naturally, given sufficient time. If another colloid with the opposite charge is added to the young wine, the oppositely charged molecules attract each other and form a solid precipitate which can be removed either by allowing it to settle, or by filtration. This cannot be achieved by filtration alone, because the colloidal molecules are too small to be retained by even the finest of filters. Fining and filtration are not interchangeable, but are complementary: fining removes colloids, whereas filtration removes solid particles, including those formed as a result of fining.

1 The negatively charged
fining agent is added

2 The molecules clump
together immediately

10.2 The action of fining

The one problem which can occur is that if excess fining agent is added, the fining agent itself could precipitate with time, so it is important that no more than the correct amount is added. This can easily be determined by a simple experiment. A row of bottles is prepared, each containing the same amount of wine. To each bottle in succession is added a larger quantity of fining agent. The bottles are then shaken to mix the contents and left to stand. By observing the level of the deposit in each bottle, it can be ascertained when an increased quantity of fining agent has no further effect.

This will be the correct fining rate, where the quantity of added colloid exactly matches the amount of protein to be removed from the wine. By multiplication, the correct quantity for the whole vat can be calculated, the powder weighed out, dispersed in a few litres of wine and added to the vat. After stirring thoroughly, the wine is left to stand until the deposit has fallen to the bottom, after which it is racked off into a clean vat.

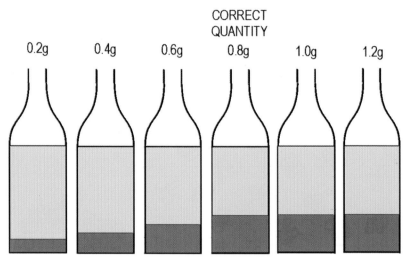

10.3 The results of a fining trial

Most of the fining agents are themselves proteinaceous substances, obtained from natural sources: albumin from egg white, egg white itself, gelatine from bones and hides, casein from milk, isinglass from sturgeon. All have molecules with the opposite electrostatic charge to the charge on the wine colloids.

There is one widely used fining agent that is not a colloid, and that is bentonite, which is an earth that is mined in Wyoming, Tennessee. (Bentonite should not be confused with kieselguhr, which is a filtration aid and not a fining agent. See p.107) Bentonite consists of an alumino-silicate clay, whose small particles acquire a negative charge when dispersed in wine and are thus ideal for removing the positively charged protein molecules. The advantage of using bentonite is that there is no danger of over-fining, but set against this is the fact that it has strong powers of adsorption and can reduce the fruit of the wine in both aroma and flavour. Also, it forms a voluminous, gelatinous deposit from which it is difficult to recover the wine, so excessive use results in wasted wine. Despite its popularity, bentonite is not a substance that should be used carelessly.

The other, and no less important, reason for fining is to improve the taste or appearance of wines by the removal of excess tannin or other astringent constituent, as witness the still widely used practice of the addition of egg-white to many classed growth clarets. Each fining agent has its own particular property and can be used for making a specific improvement in the wine.

FINING AGENT	SOURCE	WINE	REMOVES
Bentonite	Earth mining	All	Proteins
Egg whites, albumin	Eggs	Red	Tannin
Gelatine	Bones, hides	Red, white	Phenolics
Isinglass	Fish swim bladders	White	Tannin
Milk or casein	Milk	White	Colour, tannin
PVPP	Manufactured	White	Phenolics
Silica sol	Manufactured	White	Fining agents

Blue fining, which is not true fining, as it is not the removal of unstable colloids, is dealt with under Chemical Additives (see p.136).

The topic of fining is somewhat emotive, engendering concern amongst those involved with ingredient listing legislation, and amongst those who do not wish to consume animal products. Whilst some vegetarians will happily eat eggs or milk, vegans do not consume anything that is based on any product of animal origin. By the very nature of the fining process, the finished wine does not contain any of these substances, even if they have been used, because all of the fining agent will have been removed by reacting with the colloids in the wine. Fining agents should be regarded as processing aids, not ingredients. This may well be true, but how do we know that this is the case? Only if the wine were submitted for advanced and expensive analysis would we know whether the wine is truly free from added fining agent. The subject will remain controversial so long as finings based on animal products are used. The only sure solution to this problem is to used only bentonite – or no finings at all.

Filtration

The process of filtration probably causes more controversy than any other single treatment available to the winemaker. There are those who maintain that filtration ruins wine; there is the opposite school which claims that, properly applied, there is no ill effect whatsoever. The fact is that filtration, properly used, with care and expertise, has no deleterious effect on the wine. On the other hand, it is not necessarily an essential process.

Filtration is a widely varied technique that can be applied for different purposes. Coarse filtration will render a cloudy wine bright. A fine filtration will remove all micro-organisms, if necessary. If a wine has been blended in the medium dry or off-dry style, with a small quantity of residual sugar, it will have to be packed in an aseptic manner (see p.178), with a total absence of yeast, to prevent a re-fermentation in bottle. In this instance, filtration is an essential treatment before bottling.

Conversely, filtration is not necessary for traditionally made wines because they are intrinsically stable once in a hermetically sealed bottle. Yeasts and bacteria will die out due to the combined effects of a shortage of both nutrients and oxygen. Oxidation is prevented provided the cork is sound, and the wine will keep until the end of its natural life, the only change being the maturation reactions (see below).

The greatest danger with filtration is being over-zealous, using sheets that are too tight in structure or membranes with pore sizes intended for the preparation intravenous liquids. Properly applied, the sequence of filtrations forms a widely used and very satisfactory system for the bottling of good quality commercial wines.

Filtration is normally applied in a graded fashion, using coarse filtration first, to remove the gross particles, followed by progressively finer stages of filtration, until the wine has been brought into the correct state for bottling. The reason for this progression is that, apart from cross-flow filtration (see below), the finer types of filter would be blocked by an excessive quantity of solids.

Principles of filtration

Filtration techniques fall into two main categories, depth filtration and surface, or absolute, filtration.

Depth filtration is so called because the solid particles are removed from the liquid within the structure of the filter medium itself, rather than on the surface. The filter medium has to be many times thicker than the size of the particles being removed, because the channels through the filter are mostly bigger than the particles themselves. The filter works because the particles become trapped somewhere within the depth of the material, as they travel through the tortuous pathways, before they can reach the clean side.

10.4 Yeast cells trapped by a sheet filter

The advantage of this type of filtration is that it can cope with liquids that are heavily laden with solid particles, such as juice straight from the press, or wine that has just finished its fermentation. The mass of solid particles is held somewhere within the depth of the filter, which gradually blocks, until eventually it has to be discarded.

The commonest forms of depth filtration used in the wine industry are kieselguhr (or earth filtration) and sheets (or pad filtration), both of which are widely used. They are simple to operate, and the expendable filter media are of relatively low cost. However, the disadvantage of this type of filtration is that it is not totally secure. By trying to filter too quickly, or by using the filter too long without replacing the filter medium, it is possible to force particles through the filter to the clean side. Hence the development of absolute filtration.

10.5 Principles of filtration

Absolute, or surface, filtration gives complete safety, the channels through the filter medium being smaller than the particles being removed. The particles are removed at the surface of the filter, rather than within its depth, hence the name, surface filtration. The alternative name of absolute filtration is equally valid because the particles absolutely cannot get through the filter. The disadvantage is that the holes are easily blocked by solid matter, which prevents further filtration.

This category of filtration is widely used in the wine bottling industry in the form of the membrane, or cartridge, filter. Because of its tendency to block very easily, it is only used as the final guard filter immediately prior to the filling machine.

Kieselguhr filtration (earth filtration)

Depth filtration using kieselguhr is the first type of filtration used on wines that are thick with solid particles from the fermentation. These solids consist of a mixture of dead yeast cells with some live cells, solid matter from the original grape and other solids which have been rendered insoluble by the effect of the alcohol.

Kieselguhr is an earth that is mined in Germany and consists of the skeletal remains of diatoms, tiny sea creatures that inhabited the North Sea many millions of years ago, when that part of Germany was under the water. The deposits are mined, ground into a fine powder and treated with acids and alkalis until all that remains is pure silica, which is totally inert. When these particles have been formed into a bed they produce an effective filter by forming a porous barrier whose channels are numerous and tortuous.

This substance is used in two types of filter, which are used for the first filtration of wine after the fermentation has finished. In both cases, the kieselguhr is made into a slurry with water or wine and is dosed into the cloudy wine as it reaches the filter.

10.6 Kieselguhr, showing diatoms

10.7 A rotary vacuum filter

The *rotary vacuum filter* is the machine of choice for the first stage, as it can cope with liquids which are almost too thick to be called liquid. This filter consists of a large horizontal drum whose cylindrical surface is formed from a fine stainless steel mesh. The lower half of the drum is immersed in a bath containing the cloudy wine. When in operation the drum rotates slowly, the interior of the drum being connected to a powerful vacuum pump. The vacuum draws the wine through the mesh into the interior of the drum, from whence it is pumped out.

At this stage, effective filtration is not occurring because the mesh of the drum is not sufficiently fine to trap the particles that make the wine cloudy, but it will trap particles of kieselguhr. The bed of kieselguhr has to be built up by re-circulating the wine and adding more kieselguhr. As the vacuum sucks the wine through the mesh, the kieselguhr is gradually deposited, and with each successive rotation of the drum, the layer gets thicker until an effective bed has been formed. At this point, true filtration begins, valves are changed over and the filtered wine is pumped into a clean vat. To enable the filter to work continuously, a blade shaves off the top layer of kieselguhr as the drum rotates, thus removing the outer layer of wine deposits and preventing the bed from becoming too thick.

The rotary vacuum filter is used primarily for filtering the lees, which no other filter could handle. It does have the disadvantage that the large surface area of the filter bed is exposed to air, with the inevitable risk of oxidation. Hence, the development of the enclosed types of filter, which has no particular name other than *earth filter*. It is totally enclosed and can be flushed with nitrogen before use. Inside, it consists of a series of rotating hollow disks with a mesh surface, which operate by exactly the same principle as the rotary vacuum filter.

10.8 An enclosed earth filter opened for cleaning

Kieselguhr can be purchased in a variety of particle sizes, giving filtration of all grades, from simple clarification up to yeast removal. Although the filter machine is expensive to purchase, it is versatile, can easily be wheeled around the winery, and kieselguhr is cheap. Such filters are widely used for preparing wine for subsequent stages of treatment, and can even remove yeast if the finest grade of kieselguhr is used (sometimes known as *terre rose*, or pink earth, because of its colour).

Sheet filtration (plate & frame filtration)

Another form of depth filtration is used after the gross solid matter has been removed from the wine, variously known as a sheet filter, a pad filter or a plate and frame filter. The last of these is a good descriptive title because the filter consists of a solid, heavy framework with a fixed back plate and a moveable front plate, which can be wound in and out by a large screw thread. Between these two end plates is a set of specially designed chambers known as 'plates' which distribute the wine to the filter sheets that are placed between each of the plates in a sandwich formation. The important point to note is that the wine does not pass from one end of the filter to the other, through all the sheets, but is distributed by the plates in such a way that each portion of wine passes through one sheet only. The cloudy wine enters the filter on one side (shown blue in diagram 10.10 opposite), is distributed to the sheets, passes through them and collects as bright wine on the other side of the filter (shown red in the diagram). The reason for having multiple sheets is merely to increase the rate at which the wine can be filtered: the more sheets, the greater the flow rate, but the quality of the filtration remains the same.

10.9 1A traditional sheet filter

10.10 Mode of operation of a sheet filter

The sheets themselves are of quite simple construction, consisting primarily of ordinary cellulose fibres, the same as blotting paper. They may contain extra substances to increase their filtration efficiency, such as kieselguhr, but they no longer contain asbestos, which was banned in the 1970s as being a potential carcinogen. In some ways, this was a pity because asbestos is a very efficient filter aid, and is harmless if handled with care. As with earth filtration, filter sheets depend upon the thickness of the sheet being many times greater than the size of the particles being removed.

By using filter sheets of a very fine grade, it is possible to remove even the micro-organisms from wine and render it sterile. Such sheets are therefore known as sterilising sheets and are frequently used for removing yeasts and bacteria before bottling the wine. But therein lies a danger, because this type of filtration is depth filtration and, due to the structure of the sheet, with its mat of fibres and comparatively large interstices, it is possible, by mishandling the operation, to force yeasts right through the sheet and into the filtered wine. Thus, operators using sheet filtration need thorough training, to ensure they understand that the stated maximum flow rate and maximum pressure differential between the inlet and outlet of the filter must not be exceeded.

10.11 Fibrous sheet filter material

Despite this drawback, sheet filters are widely used, although the initial capital outlay is high. These machines have to be made of very substantial components to withstand the high forces required to compress the edges of the sheets to prevent leakage. However, the sheets are inexpensive, and are obtainable in all grades from simple clarification (polishing) up to total sterilisation. Successful filtration depends on the correct selection of sheets for each type of wine.

One of the least attractive aspects of the traditional sheet filter is the dripping edges of the sheets, which attract flies and look generally unhygienic. This has led to the development of totally enclosed versions, where the filter elements are enclosed in a cylindrical stainless steel housing, which greatly improves the cleanliness of their operation. This equipment, incidentally, looks remarkably like a membrane installation, so care should be taken when visiting a winery to avoid making a wrong judgement regarding their filtration technique.

Membrane filtration (Cartridge filtration)

The shortcomings of depth filtration, the clumsiness of the equipment and the uncertainty of filtration efficiency have led to the development of an absolute filter, the membrane. This has quite the opposite characteristics to earlier forms of filter, in that it does not rely on a depth of material but filters at the surface of the medium. This comprises a thin plastic membrane punctured with minute holes, which are smaller than the particles being removed. (This is a simplistic description of the structure of a membrane, which is actually quite complex, but it will suffice for understanding its function.)

10.12 Photomicrograph of a membrane filter

The membrane is fragile, so has to be supported on a layer of fibrous material which is then folded into a concertina formation and is sealed into a cylindrical former, looking somewhat like a car oil filter. This is fitted with a rubber O-ring and is plugged into a suitable hole in a solid metal base-plate and the whole covered with a stainless steel housing. The housing is filled with wine and the pressure of the pump forces the wine through the cartridge from the outside to the inside, where it collects and is removed via the base of the unit.

10.13 Membrane cartridges

This would appear to solve the problems of the removal of particles from wine, but unfortunately there is a drawback. Because these filters have no depth and the filtration takes place at the surface, the holes become blocked very quickly, and the flow comes to a total stop. Therefore, the operation of a membrane filter must be handled with great care, and it must only be used for the final filtration of wine that is already very clean. Any attempt to filter a dirty wine will result in an expensive change of cartridges.

The costs of membrane filtration are opposite to depth filtration in that the equipment for housing the cartridges is relatively cheap, but the cartridges are expensive. However, properly handled, the running costs of membrane filtration are not high because each cartridge will filter thousands, if not millions, of litres of wine without blocking. They are universally used as the final guard filter prior to the bottling of wine, when they should correctly be placed immediately prior to the filling machine, to trap any stray yeasts that might have escaped the sterilisation process.

10.14 Cross-section through a membrane cartridge

Membranes are manufactured in a range of different pore sizes, and an effective way of maximising their life is to use them in sequence, the wine passing from larger pore size to smallest. Alternatively, most membrane filter manufacturers supply what is known as a "guard filter" to protect the final membrane. This filter contains cartridges that look like membranes, but are actually made of fibrous material which acts as a depth filter and removes the particles that would clog the membrane. Being depth filters, and not absolute filters, these guard filters are given nominal ratings, such '2µm nominal'. This is a useful way of differentiating a guard filter from a true membrane.

The largest size usually encountered in wineries is 1.2µm, which will remove most yeasts, but allows bacteria to pass. (µm = micrometre, µm = micron, both of which equal one millionth of a metre) This might be followed by a 0.8µm, which removes all yeasts, but does not guarantee the removal of all bacteria. The final membrane is normally 0.45µm, which removes all yeast and all bacteria. It is possible to obtain a 0.2µm pore size, but this is not advisable for wine filtration and should be reserved for the production of sterile water. The danger here is that the pore size is so small that it could remove some of the valuable constituents from the wine itself.

10.15 Membrane filter housings

A good principle adopted by some wineries is to relate the pore size to the wine being filtered. The wines which are the most susceptible to microbial damage, such as light German wines containing less alcohol and high residual sugars, need the most stringent filtration. In this case, a 0.45µm might well be used. Conversely, it would be advisable to filter a full-bodied dry red wine through a 0.8µm cartridge, to ensure that the body of the wine is not being adversely affected.

10.16 Yeast cells on a membrane filter

Cross-flow filtration

The problem of the short life of a membrane in the presence of solid particles has been overcome by cross-flow filtration, an ingenious modification to the technique of filtration.   In all the filtration methods discussed above, the flow of liquid is perpendicular to surface of the filter, so all the solid particles collect on the filter, gradually blocking it (or in the case of a membrane, instantly blocking it).   By the simple expedient of turning the flow through ninety degrees, so that it is parallel to the surface rather than perpendicular to it, the liquid will flow across the surface of the membrane and will sweep the surface clean rather than blocking it. By arranging for the wine to flow in a complete circuit on the dirty side of the membrane, the wine can circulate repeatedly past the membrane.   Under the pressure of the pump, some of the liquid will pass through the pores, but the solid particles are held in suspension on the dirty side, instead of blocking the membrane.   The result is filtration of the wine, with a progressive concentration of solids on the dirty side, which can gradually be bled off.

PERPENDICULAR FLOW
BLINDS MEMBRANE
SURFACE

CROSS FLOW KEEPS
MEMBRANE SURFACE
CLEAR

10.17 The principle of cross-flow filtration

The great advantage of this type of filtration is that the dirtiest of wine, straight from the fermentation vat and heavily loaded with yeast cells and other solid matter can be filtered to bottling standard in one pass.   It is equally useful in the cleaning of must before fermentation.   The disadvantage is that the machine is very expensive, containing many membrane units, either in the form of rectangular cells, or formed into fibres which are enclosed in tubes.

But this cost must be set against the cost of multiple filtrations, using different styles of filter, and the risk to the quality of the wine through multiple handling.

10.18 A cross-flow filter machine

Ultra-filtration

Membranes can be produced with pores much smaller than the smallest in general use, so small that they will actually filter out individual components of wine, the tannins, the sugars and the acids.

10.19 An ultra-filtration unit

By the use of this technique, wine can be separated into its essential constituents – sugars, acids, tannins, colours etc. – so wine in all its different colours and styles could be produced from one large tank of base wine. This is the ultimate in filtration technique, hence the name of ultra-filtration. It is, however, illegal in Europe (and probably in other parts of the world) and is only used as a research tool, but its very existence poses a threat, if only in theory. What will happen in the future? Shall we need only to produce large volumes of one wine, which can then be manipulated to produce all the different wine styles to order?

Considerable research is going on in many parts of the wine world, with the development of new methods of vinification. This is not a cause for any concern: indeed, it is quite the reverse. The production of wine has never been more exciting, with advanced scientific techniques blending with tradition. The quality of wine has never been higher, and the value for money has never been so good.

Tartrate stabilisation

The removal of unstable colloids and solid particles yields a clear, bright wine. Unfortunately, this does not mean that the wine is totally stable and will not deposit any further solid matter. The chances are high that, at a later date, it will deposit tartrate crystals in the bottle. Although these crystals are entirely natural and totally harmless, the average consumer will object to them and will return the bottle with a serious complaint. An attempt, therefore, has to be made to prevent this happening, but it is not easy to guarantee success and it is probably the biggest problem facing all wine producers. No supplier is prepared to give a warranty that their wine will never deposit tartrate crystals.

The mechanism of crystal formation is complex because it is dependent upon a combination of the relative concentrations in the wine of potassium, calcium, tartaric acid, alcohol and pH. The presence of colloids also has a great effect on tartrate stability because the colloids act as protective agents, preventing the formation of crystals. Before commencing any of the tartrate stabilisation processes, it is essential that a thorough fining operation is carried out. Incomplete removal of colloids is probably the reason for the failure of many stabilisation processes, with the resultant crystals in the bottle and the accompanying expense of a product re-call. (See p.19 for more detail.)

Cold stabilisation

In the traditional process of cold stabilisation, the wine is chilled to just above its freezing point, which is -4°C for a wine of 12% alcohol and as low as -8°C for a fortified wine, and is then stored in insulated tanks for up to eight days. This is expensive in terms of capital outlay for the refrigeration unit and a bank of insulated tanks, uses a large amount of energy for chilling and involves an expensive stock holding. What is more, the results are not always reliable.

The process depends upon crystallisation being initiated by any minute particles that happen to be present that can act as nuclei. Once small crystals have formed, further crystallisation occurs at the surface of the crystals, which gradually grow bigger. The process is inefficient because the deposited crystals lie in the bottom of the tank, with convection currents being the only means by which the contents of the tank come into contact with the crystals.

10.20 A cold stabilisation installation

The weakness of this process is that colloids and other components in the wine have a very big influence on the efficiency of the crystallisation process. They have a protective effect on the micro-crystals, preventing further deposition. The result is that, at the end of the cold treatment, the concentration of potassium bi-tartrate in solution has not been reduced sufficiently to guarantee stability after bottling. Later in the life of the wine, when the colloids have ceased to have their protective effect, the crystals form inside the bottle. Hence, the critical importance of an efficient fining process before refrigeration.

Contact process

This weakness in the old static process led to the development of the contact process, which has proved to be quicker, cheaper and more effective. It gets its name from the principle of bringing the wine into contact with micro-crystals of potassium bi-tartrate, which act as nuclei, enabling the crystallisation to occur more readily. The process starts with the chilling of the wine, but not to the low temperatures required by the traditional process: 0°C is usually sufficient. Finely ground crystals of potassium bi-tartrate are added

10.21 Contact process equipment

and the wine stirred vigorously for one to two hours. The vigorous stirring keeps the crystals in suspension, thus ensuring close contact with the wine, so that they can function by drawing out the excess tartrate, growing bigger in the process. At the end of the stabilisation, the wine is filtered while still cold, and the crystals are separated out, ground down and added to the next batch of wine.

The latest development is the continuous contact process, where the crystals are packed into the conical base of a vertical tank and the cooled wine is pumped upwards through the crystal bed. At the top of the tank, the stabilised wine can be drawn off. Periodically, the tank has to be opened and the enlarged bed of crystals removed.

Ion exchange

The process of ion exchange has been used in the domestic situation for many years in the form of the water softener, which consists of a container packed with an ion exchange resin. This resin is a form of plastic, which contains loosely bonded sodium ions. Hard water contains calcium and magnesium salts, which are the cause of the hardness. When the water flows past the particles of resin, the calcium and magnesium in the water are attracted to the resin, being replaced by the sodium ions from the resin. When the resin is saturated with calcium and magnesium, brine, which is a solution of common salt or sodium chloride, is passed through the resin bed. Now the reverse happens: the sodium goes on to the resin and the calcium and magnesium come off, and are flushed down the drain.

In the treatment of wine, a similar process occurs: the potassium and calcium in the wine are attracted to the resin and are replaced by the sodium ions. The wine now contains sodium bi-tartrate. This prevents the formation of tartrate crystals, because sodium bi-tartrate is much more soluble than the calcium and potassium salts. Thus, ion exchange is the prevention of crystallisation, whereas refrigeration methods rely on the removal of excess tartrates.

10.22 An ion exchange unit in Australia

Unfortunately, from a health aspect, it is not a good thing to replace potassium with sodium. It is common knowledge that excessive salt is bad for the body, especially in relation to cardio-vascular conditions. We are all told not to put too much salt on our food. One of the simple counter measures is to administer a potassium salt, such as potassium chloride, which replaces the sodium in the body and rectifies the situation. Wine is one of the richest sources of dietary potassium and must be a much more pleasurable way of taking potassium than swallowing potassium chloride tablets! Here we have yet another of the benefits of drinking wine, and not merely for pleasure. Ion exchange removes this health-giving element and replaces it with an unwelcome entity, so it is not surprising that the use of ion exchange is prohibited within the European Union, although many other countries of the world do use it. It shoould be noted that wine which has been ion-exchanged should not be put up for sale within the EU.

Footnote

Although none of the above treatments, if properly carried out, has a noticeably damaging effect on the quality of the wine, the best philosophy is to use the minimum treatment possible. The principle of 'low intervention' winemaking, as this is known, is undoubtedly the correct approach. However small the effect might be, in every stage of handling there is the potential for a loss of quality.

Chapter 11

CHEMICAL ADDITIVES

The best use of bad wine is to drive away poor relations.

French proverb

The additives allowed for wine, in common with those allowed for any foodstuff, are strictly limited by regulations which vary from country to country. Well-made wine is a fairly stable product and should not need additives, other than those to combat oxidation and the attack of micro-organisms, and even these are not necessarily essential. From a food safety angle, it is comforting to know that virtually no pathogen can survive in wine because of the presence of alcohol and the natural acidity.

Sulphur dioxide

This most useful of all additives has been known for centuries, long before its action was fully understood. Sulphur is an element with the chemical symbol S, which is found in the earth's crust in volcanic regions and is a pale yellow brittle rock-like substance. Surprisingly, when ignited it burns with a blue flame, the yellow solid melting to a viscous orange liquid. However, more is happening, as soon becomes apparent, when a lung-full of a noxious pungent gas is inhaled, causing severe breathing problems, resembling an attack of asthma. The gas is sulphur dioxide and is formed according to the following equation:

$$S \quad + \quad O_2 \quad \rightarrow \quad SO_2$$
sulphur $\quad$ oxygen $\quad$ sulphur dioxide

Sulphur dioxide gas is soluble in water, actually reacting with it to produce sulphurous acid:

$$SO_2 \quad + \quad H_2O \quad \rightarrow \quad H_2SO_3$$
sulphur dioxide $\quad$ water $\quad$ sulphurous acid

This is the sequence of events that caused the so-called "acid rain" that was being produced in England before the power stations cleaned up their flue gasses. Residual sulphur in the fuel oil was burned in the furnaces, producing sulphur dioxide which was released into the atmosphere. It was alleged that this made its way to Scandinavia, where it dissolved in the rain, producing sulphurous acid which destroyed conifer forests. Irrespective of the scientific facts behind this allegation, the power stations have installed expensive equipment to remove the sulphur dioxide before the flue gasses are released from the top of the chimney.

It can be seen that the colloquial use by winemakers of the word 'sulphuring' is misleading because it is not sulphur that is being added, but sulphur dioxide. This habit has undoubtedly grown up due to the fact that, long before the chemical industry was born, sulphur dioxide was produced on the spot by burning sulphur. Empty casks were sterilised after rinsing by lowering a piece of burning sulphur into the cask. The sulphur dioxide produced by this reaction dissolves in the residual water in the cask, thus sterilising it. Although sulphur candles are still used, the simplest way of obtaining sulphur dioxide is by using potassium metabisulphite, a white powder with the chemical formula $K_2S_2O_5$. This substance has the useful property of releasing sulphur dioxide when dissolved in an acid aqueous liquid, which is precisely the constitution of grape must and wine. Under these conditions it releases 57% of its weight as sulphur dioxide. Alternatively, pure sulphur dioxide can be purchased in cylinders as the liquefied gas, from whence it can be metered into the wine (and this process can even be automated). This method is particularly useful for direct addition to wine, using specially designed dosing equipment, which can be adjusted to give exactly the right concentration.

Although toxic in large doses, sulphur dioxide is harmless when used at the correct level. It is, in fact, used in many different foodstuffs as an antioxidant and a preservative. It can be found in dried fruit, fruit juices and squashes, fresh fruit salads, sausages, peeled potatoes and many more foodstuffs. In Europe its presence can be recognised in ingredient lists by its 'E number', which can be anything from E220 to E227, depending on the additive used.

Although a very useful additive, it does have its disadvantages in that it can cause an allergic reaction in some consumers who are prone to asthma or other allergies. Such people have to be aware that most wines contain this substance, hence the labelling regulation in the USA that demands the statement, 'This wine contains sulphites'. The unfortunate fact is that virtually all wine contains natural sulphites because traces are produced by yeasts during fermentation. The World Health Organisation has conducted a study on the total sulphur dioxide in the diet and has concluded that the present levels are within safe limits.

A second disadvantage is that sulphur dioxide bleaches the colour of red wine and can also result in a loss of fruit, although the wine does partially recover with time, when the level of free sulphur dioxide has diminished naturally. The good winemaker always uses sulphur dioxide sparingly.

Sulphur dioxide has become such a universal additive because it has four quite distinct properties:

1 Antioxidant

The principle use of sulphur dioxide is the prevention of oxidation, the antioxidant property. In wine production, it is now realised that oxidation must be kept to the minimum if fruit is to be conserved.

The prime reason for the anti-oxidant property of sulphur dioxide is that it will readily combine with oxygen, thus removing it before too much harm can be done. A product of this reaction is that familiar schooldays chemical, sulphuric acid, which might seem a totally inappropriate substance to find in wine, but the concentration is very low, amounting to a few parts per million. At this level, sulphuric acid is harmless. Only at much higher concentration does it become aggressive and dangerous.

$$H_2SO_3 \quad + \quad [O] \quad \rightarrow \quad H_2SO_4$$
$$\text{sulphurous acid} \qquad \text{oxygen} \qquad \text{sulphuric acid}$$

[Certain aspects some of the equations shown are not strictly correct, in chemical terms, but have been simplified to show the principles of the function of sulphur dioxide.]

Although sulphur dioxide will scavenge any oxygen that becomes dissolved in the wine, the reaction is not immediate. It is possible for oxygen and sulphur dioxide to exist together in the wine, before reaction takes place, and herein lies the danger. It is during this time that oxygen can do damage to the wine, so it is far better to ensure that oxygen and wine never come into contact by careful handling and by the total exclusion of air. Sulphur dioxide is thus not the excuse for poor wine handling techniques.

The level of sulphur dioxide has to be checked many times during the processing and handling operations, because its action is self-destructive. Every atom of oxygen destroys a molecule of sulphur dioxide, resulting in a constantly falling concentration. A particularly important moment is in the preparation of wine for bottling, for it is critical for the keeping qualities of the bottled wine (particularly wines for everyday drinking) that the sulphur dioxide is adjusted to the correct level.

2 Antiseptic (anti-microbial)

Septic wounds are caused by bacteria infecting the surrounding tissue, where they can flourish in the warmth and the damp nutritious surroundings. When an antiseptic is applied to a wound, the bacteria are killed. Sulphur dioxide has the same effect on bacteria in wine: they are easily killed because they are sensitive towards sulphur dioxide, which is most fortuitous since acetobacter is probably the commonest bacterium to attack wine, turning it to vinegar.

Acetobacter are aerobic bacteria, and need oxygen to flourish. A dose of sulphur dioxide followed by filtration is the immediate treatment for any wine that has such an infection. The sulphur dioxide will initiate a two-pronged attack by poisoning the bacteria and by removing any remaining oxygen that the bacteria need if they are to thrive.

The antiseptic property of sulphur dioxide is also used to prevent the malo-lactic fermentation. In this instance it attacks the lactobacillus, a bacterium which converts malic acid to lactic acid. (See p.66)

Yeasts are more tolerant of sulphur dioxide, but this tolerance varies from strain to strain, which provides a useful way of selectively subduing the less desirable ones that, fortuitously, tend to be less tolerant. The addition of sulphur dioxide before fermentation reduces the activity of wild yeasts and permits the wine yeasts to take over at an earlier stage, which gives a better and more secure fermentation.

It is a common misconception that sulphur dioxide at bottling is used to prevent a re-fermentation. Wine yeasts can tolerate a far higher level of sulphur dioxide than would be desirable, either for reasons of taste, or to keep within the legal limits for total sulphur dioxide. Some micro-organisms might have their reproductive rate slowed down, but the principal reason for using sulphur dioxide at bottling is for its anti-oxidative property.

3 Anti-oxidasic

The third property of sulphur dioxide relates to enzymes. The oxidation of fruits and fruit products is a slow process in the absence of any catalyst. (A catalyst is a substance that enables a chemical reaction to proceed, but does not itself take part in the reaction.) However, we know from the observation of fruits such as apples that, when they are cut or bitten, they brown very rapidly, indicating that something must be present that can hasten this reaction. Indeed, there is something present acting as a catalyst, and that catalyst is an enzyme.

All enzymes are catalysts, and all life depends on enzymes. If they are destroyed, life ceases. The reason that cyanide is such a deadly and rapid poison is that it poisons the enzymes in our bodies.

Enzymes are named by words ending in -ase; thus, the enzymes that promote oxidation are known as oxidases. Sulphur dioxide acts as a poison to the oxidases (of which there are many different varieties), greatly reducing the rate of oxidation, adding further to its antioxidant property. In fact, sulphur dioxide is used commercially to preserve things like fresh fruit salad, where it prevents the browning of white-fleshed fruits such as apples and pears. When added to wine, it has the same effect and prevents the browning of white wines. Caution is needed, however, as sulphur dioxide is toxic at high concentrations, and people have died after eating fresh fruit salad which has been carelessly dosed with sulphur dioxide.

4 Corrective after oxidation

The first three properties of sulphur dioxide are all preventative, but there is a fourth property that is corrective, in that it can freshen tired wines which are suffering from a slight degree of oxidation. Wines in such a condition have probably been badly handled and have lost their entire free sulphur dioxide. The first action when dealing with such a wine is to analyse it and to make a suitable addition of sulphur dioxide to restore it to its correct level. However, this does more than simply protect it against further oxidation, it actually improves the taste of the wine by refreshing it.

The reason for this is that one of the main products of the oxidation of alcohol is acetaldehyde, which is a predominant component of the characteristic sherry nose, which is a deliberately oxidised wine. When added to a tired wine, sulphur dioxide combines with acetaldehyde, converting it into an odourless and tasteless bisulphite compound, thus removing any hint of oxidation and restoring the wine (almost) to its youthful nature.

$$CH_3CH_2OH \quad + \quad [O] \quad \rightarrow \quad CH_3CHO \quad + \quad H_2O$$
$$\text{ethanol} \qquad \text{oxygen} \quad \text{acetaldehyde} \quad \text{water}$$

$$CH_3CHO \quad + \quad SO_2 \quad \rightarrow \quad \text{tasteless bisulphite compound}$$

It is important to realise that sulphur dioxide is not the 'magic potion' that will correct all bad wines and bad winemaking. Good technique is necessary at all times. Sulphur dioxide merely helps to maintain quality: it cannot create it where it is absent.

Free and total sulphur dioxide

Sulphur dioxide in wine cannot be discussed without reference to 'the free and total', an expression commonly used by winemakers. To understand the significance of free sulphur dioxide and total sulphur dioxide, it is necessary to understand a little chemistry.

Sulphur dioxide is a reactive substance and will combine not only with oxygen, but also with other natural substances in the wine, such as sugars, aldehydes and ketones. When combined with these substances, the sulphur dioxide no longer possesses any of its protective properties and is known as the combined, or bound, or fixed sulphur dioxide. Badly made wines and oxidised wines have a higher proportion of aldehydes and ketones than wine in good condition, which results in a greater proportion of the sulphur dioxide becoming combined. The more that is combined, the less is available for its prime purpose of protecting the wine.

$$SO_2 \quad + \quad ketones \quad \rightarrow \quad bisulphite\ compounds$$

That portion of the sulphur dioxide that is not combined is known, logically, as the free sulphur dioxide. This is the active substance that has the protective properties.

The sum of the free sulphur dioxide and the bound sulphur dioxide makes up the total sulphur dioxide, which is also logical.

$$Free\ SO_2 \quad + \quad Bound\ SO_2 \quad = \quad Total\ SO_2$$

The total sulphur dioxide is regulated by EU law. In the stomach much of the bound sulphur dioxide is released by the acid and the warmth of the stomach contents, and so is free to do its damage to the body if present above the safe limit. The basic legal limit for wine is 160 mg per litre, which is the level applied to dry red wine, that is a red wine containing not more than 4 grams per litre of residual sugars. It was recognised that white wine needs more protection than red wine, because the latter contains its own natural anti-oxidants, the polyphenols. So white wine is allowed an extra 50 mg per litre. Further, because of the binding power of sugars, another 50 mg per litre is allowed for wine containing not less than 5 mg per litre of residual sugars.

Still greater quantities of sulphur dioxide are allowed for the natural sweet wines of the world, which has resulted in a plethora of different legal limits for the many different wine styles.

EU LIMITS FOR TOTAL SULPHUR DIOXIDE	
• Dry red wine	160 mg/l
• Dry white wine	210
• Red wine with 5 g sugar/litre or more	210
• White wine with 5g sugar/litre or more	260
• Spätlese, white Bordeaux Supérieur etc	300
• Auslese etc	350
• Trockenbeerenauslese, Beerenauslese, Ausbruch, Sauternes, Bonnezeaux, Graves Supérieures etc	400

Years ago, in the days of bad winemaking, wines contained high levels of binding substances produced by poor techniques. It was sometimes a problem to maintain sufficient free sulphur dioxide without exceeding the legal limit for the total (which was higher then, in any case). Thankfully, the situation has improved greatly, and this is no longer a problem. The progressive reduction in the permitted limit of total sulphur dioxide was undoubtedly one of the factors that forced winemakers in many parts of Europe to improve their techniques.

Molecular sulphur dioxide

There is yet more to the sulphur dioxide story, because the free sulphur dioxide exists in more than one form.

When dissolved in wine or water, a chemical reaction takes place between the sulphur dioxide and the water, forming sulphurous acid.

$$SO_2 \quad + \quad H_2O \quad \longleftrightarrow \quad H_2SO_3$$

This acid, in common with all other acids, actually exists in solution in the ionised form, where the molecule splits into a positive ion and a negative ion:

$$H_2SO_3 \quad \longleftrightarrow \quad H^+ \quad + \quad HSO_3^-$$

Both of these reactions can go in either direction, indicated by the double-headed arrow in the middle of the equation. Thus, the two ions can re-combine to form un-ionised sulphurous acid, which itself can decompose into water and sulphur dioxide.

$$H^+ + HSO_3^- \quad \rightarrow \quad H_2SO_3 \quad \rightarrow \quad H_2O \quad + \quad SO_2$$

This sulphur dioxide is known as the molecular sulphur dioxide, because it is present as simple un-ionised sulphur dioxide, and is best imagined as the gaseous molecule floating around unaltered in the liquid.

The purpose of this foray into chemistry is to gain an understanding of the true nature of the way in which sulphur dioxide works. It is only the molecular form that possesses the protective properties, and not the entire free sulphur dioxide. The proportion of this form increases as the pH of the wine gets lower, meaning a more acid wine (see p.149 for more information on pH.) Thus, acidic wines require lower doses of sulphur dioxide than those wines with higher pH and less acidity. The molecular SO_2 performs the operations of scavenging the oxygen, killing the micro-organisms, poisoning the enzymes and freshening the wine. The truly scientific winemaker will take into account the pH of the wine before deciding on the appropriate addition of sulphur dioxide.

Ascorbic acid

Ascorbic acid is the chemical name for vitamin C, the valuable vitamin found in many fresh fruits and vegetables. It has powerful antioxidant properties, which makes it a useful additive for anaerobic winemaking. It is for the same reason that it is of value in our diet, protecting our bodies against the effects of oxygen and helping to delay the ageing process.

The danger of using ascorbic acid as an anti-oxidant is that it produces hydrogen peroxide when it becomes oxidised, and hydrogen peroxide is a powerful oxidising agent. To make matters worse, the product of the oxidation of ascorbic acid is dark brown in colour, thus rendering the wine even darker than it would otherwise have been. Therefore, the use of ascorbic acid can be total disaster, with the result being far worse than if it had not been used at all. It cannot be regarded as a substitute for sulphur dioxide, but rather as reinforcement.

The way in which this effect can be prevented is to ensure that sulphur dioxide is present as a protective agent for the ascorbic acid, and under these conditions the ascorbic acid does give extra protection. There are many trained winemakers who use it regularly, especially in white wine production in countries such as Germany, New Zealand and Australia, because, properly used, it keeps the wine ultra-fresh.

Ascorbic acid has what is known as an isomeric form, erythorbic acid, which is used in Australia instead of ascorbic acid because it is cheaper, yet has similar properties. (An isomer is a substance whose molecules are mirror images of the original.) Erythorbic acid, however, is not permitted for use in wines sold in the EU, and this includes wines from Australia.

Being vitamin C, ascorbic acid is beneficial and is not harmful in any way, which makes the EU limit for wine of 150 mg/litre seem slightly odd. The human body can cope with any amount of vitamin

C, merely secreting the excess in the urine. It was Linus Pauling, the American chemist (1901 – 1994), who suggested that taking a teaspoonful of ascorbic acid every day would protect against the common cold. The only adverse reaction is possibly an attack of diarrhoea!

Sorbic acid

Sorbic acid has one property that is useful in winemaking: it stops yeast fermenting, and is used as an additive before bottling to prevent re-fermentation in bottle. It does not kill yeasts and therefore is not a fungicide, but merely prevents fermentation by interfering with the metabolism of the yeast. As it does not kill the yeast, reproduction can still carry on, ultimately producing a flocculent deposit, which would be a just cause for complaint. The more serious conditions of cloudy wine and popping corks are, however, prevented.

This property of sorbic acid is dependent on the combined presence of sulphur dioxide, alcohol and acidity, which is convenient for wine producers because all three of these conditions are satisfied. However, the efficacy drops with lower alcohol levels, demanding higher dosage rates. The EU limit is 200 mg/litre, at which level some people can begin to notice the taste of sorbic acid (and some can taste it at much lower levels), so most wine bottlers add 150 mg/litre to all wine as a compromise. At this concentration, an alcoholic strength of about 12% is required if fermentation is to be prevented. In a wine of 10.5% alcohol, this level has little protective effect, and yet susceptible wines with residual sugar, such as German wines, have habitually been bottled with the addition of sorbic acid at this level, which would seem to be pointless.

Despite the reference to the use of sorbic acid, the actual chemical added is potassium sorbate, which dissolves readily in wine and is decomposed by the acids in the wine to sorbic acid itself. The solid form of the pure acid dissolves only with difficulty.

It is important that the addition of sorbic acid is made just prior to aseptic bottling because it has no bactericidal properties whatsoever, and can be the source of an all-pervading smell of geranium leaves (strictly, pelargoniums) when metabolised by certain strains of bacteria. Wine in this condition is fit only for destruction. So it is important to ensure that wine containing sorbic acid is free from micro-organisms.

It is not surprising that its use in the quality control armoury is diminishing, with many retailers forbidding its use, not for any health implications, but merely to reduce the use of additives. It should, after all, not be necessary, because careful filtration and good hygiene are all that is required for successful aseptic bottling. The need for sorbic acid has to be an admission of a lack of confidence in the bottling process.

Metatartaric acid

Metatartaric acid is a strange substance, of no defined structure, which is produced by heating tartaric acid to a high temperature in a closed vessel. During this process the molecules partially polymerise, or bind together. It dissolves readily in water or wine and has the property of preventing the deposition of tartrate crystals, but the precise mechanism is uncertain. It is thought that it coats any micro-crystals that might be present in the wine and prevents their development to a visible size. In view of the uncertainty of refrigeration processes, this is a useful substance, and is cheap and effective.

This might seem to be the perfect answer to the prevention of tartrate crystals in the bottle, but unfortunately metatartaric acid is unstable in solution and gradually reverts to ordinary tartaric acid, resulting in the possibility of even more tartrate crystals. This happens faster under warmer conditions, as might be expected, in the knowledge that all chemical reactions proceed more quickly at higher temperatures. The effective life of metatartaric acid in wine at 25°C is about six months, whereas at 10°C it will last for eighteen months.

It is therefore ideal for wines packed in bag-in-box, which should be consumed within twelve months. The formation of tartrate crystals in this type of packaging is particularly serious, leading to leaking taps and to complaints of ruined furniture and carpets. It is of no use for the protection of wine intended for long periods of maturation in bottle.

It is also useful in those circumstances where refrigeration has not been possible, as in small wineries without sufficient capital for the installation of expensive refrigeration equipment. Indeed, there are large modern wineries that prefer to use metatartaric acid rather than cold stabilisation, which, they feel, could adversely affect the quality of the wine.

The limit imposed by EU regulations is 100 mg/litre, this being the level normally used in practice, there being little point in using less than the maximum dose.

Potassium ferrocyanide (Blue fining)

Iron and copper are elements essential to all forms of life and are found in the soil and in all foodstuff, but in excess they cause problems, so it is important that the content of these two elements in wine should be controlled. First, both iron and copper can cause a haze or even a solid deposit in wine (see p.194).

Second, copper has a yet more fateful property in that it acts as a catalyst to oxidation, a catalyst being a substance that helps another reaction to take place. In the absence of copper and the oxidising enzymes the rate of oxidation of wine is quite slow.

There is a third and very basic reason for controlling the level of copper in a wine, namely that copper is a toxic metal at higher concentrations and has a legal limit of 1 mg per litre imposed by food regulations. Many wineries used to use bronze pumps and vat fittings, and some still do! These undoubtedly contribute to an increased level of copper in the wine because the acids in the wine readily attack the bronze, which is an alloy of copper and tin.

Blue fining is a chemical process for the removal of excess iron and copper in the wine by the addition of a solution of potassium ferrocyanide, as discovered by Herr Möslinger at the beginning of the twentieth century. It is not really fining at all, because it has nothing to do with colloids or with removing proteins. The ferrocyanide reacts with any iron (Fe) and copper (Cu) that might be present in the wine, producing a deep blue deposit of ferric or cupric ferrocyanide. This simple process neatly removes the iron and the copper from the wine.

$$K_4Fe(CN)_6.3H_2O \; + \; 2Cu^{2+} \; \rightarrow \; Cu_2Fe(CN)_6 \; + \; 4K^+$$
potassium ferrocyanide   blue precipitate

The process is harmless as long as a small residual quantity of iron remains in the wine, but residual ferrocyanide should be avoided because it could be converted to cyanide, which is not exactly a pleasant substance! For this reason, blue fining can only be carried out when supervised by a qualified chemist.

There is also the slight possibility that wine containing ferrocyanide could produce a further deposit if it were to come into contact with any other source of iron or copper. However, this is unlikely in a modern winery constructed entirely of stainless steel.

Blue fining is particularly useful for removing excess copper, this being the metal that is removed first. The process can be used for all wines and is simple to apply, the only caveat being that a laboratory trial must be carried out first, the action of the ferrocyanide being somewhat unpredictable, due to the possible presence of other metal ions which might interfere.

To ensure that no excess ferrocyanide is left in the wine, the quantity of potassium ferrocyanide added is such that one to two milligrams per litre of iron is left in the wine, which guarantees that no ferrocyanide remains in solution and the wine remains harmless. Suspicion is always aroused if the analysis of the wine shows zero iron, as all wine contains some natural iron.

The sequence of actions is as follows:

1. The wine is analysed to determine the level of iron and copper.

2. The theoretical quantity of potassium ferrocyanide is calculated.

3. A sample is treated in the laboratory to determine the effect of the theoretical addition. Adjustments to this are made, as necessary.

4. The full quantity of potassium ferrocyanide is calculated and weighed out.

5. After dissolving in water, the solution is added to the wine, which is then stirred.

6. After settling, the wine is racked off the deep blue sediment, which contains the iron and copper.

Although blue fining is prohibited in many countries, in those where it is permitted, e.g. Germany, it is widely used. Its advocates claim that it has no effect on the quality of the wine, but, as with so many wine treatments, there are those who prefer not to use it because they claim that it takes out fruit as well as the metals. The best control is undoubtedly prevention rather than cure, by eliminating the source of the contamination in the first instance.

Citric acid

Citric acid is the natural acid of citrus fruits and is totally harmless, as would be expected. Its use in winemaking is for treating wines with a high level of iron, where it is not possible to carry out a blue fining operation. In these circumstances, it has the useful property of preventing iron casse by forming a soluble complex with iron, thus preventing it from forming an insoluble compound with the natural phosphates in the wine. This is a simpler option to blue fining, although in this case the iron is not removed, but merely complexed.

Citric acid is not a natural component of grape juice, and although used in some parts of the world for acidification of wine, is not allowed within the EU for that purpose, hence the EU limit of 1 g/litre. It is always added to the finished wine, and never to the unfermented juice, because it can be converted to acetic acid by the action of the yeast, resulting in a volatile wine.

Calcium phytate

Phytic acid is a naturally occurring substance found in the bran of cereals and can be used in the form of its calcium salt to remove excess iron from red wines, by precipitating it out as the very insoluble ferric phytate. A residue of phytic acid in the wine is undesirable because it combines with the essential calcium in the body, rendering it unavailable for metabolism. So the same principle applies as in blue fining, of leaving a trace of iron in the wine rather than residual calcium phytate.

Gum arabic (acacia)

Gum arabic, or gum acacia, is a substance obtained from *Acacia senegal*, a shrub native to the Sudan and is probably best known for its use as a paper glue. Chemically it is a polysaccharide and is related to the polysaccharides found in grapes. (Polysaccharides are large molecules made up of simple sugar molecules.) It is classed as a stable colloid and, as such, will stabilise the unstable colloids. (See p.99) Its use in wine is very ancient and it is added to young wine intended for early consumption to slow the precipitation of colouring matter.

Copper sulphate

It is ironic that, in these days of stainless steel equipment, there is a higher incidence of reductive taint (dirty drains or bad eggs) than with old-fashioned machinery. This is due to the fact that traces of copper from old bronze equipment, such as pumps and hose couplings, removes the hydrogen sulphide which is the source of the taint. The use of ultra-anaerobic techniques, where oxygen is never allowed to touch the wine, encourages the formation of hydrogen sulphide by the reduction of sulphur dioxide. Also, many yeasts produce traces of hydrogen sulphide from sulphur compounds during the fermentation. The complete absence of bronze components means that there are no copper ions to act as cleansing agents.

Under these circumstances, the treatment is the addition of copper in the form of copper sulphate, an attractive bright blue crystalline powder, well-known from the days of school chemistry. The quantity added must be carefully calculated, after analysis, otherwise there will be too much residual copper in the wine, necessitating a blue fining operation.

An informal demonstration of the effectiveness of copper can sometimes be useful in the tasting room. When a wine has a nose smelling of dirty drains or bad eggs, a bronze coin should be added to the glass and the wine swirled for a minute or so. If the smell disappears and the wine assumes a healthy fruity nose, hydrogen sulphide is the cause; the copper dissolved from the coin by the acids in the wine has reacted with the hydrogen sulphide and precipitated it as copper sulphide. If there is no improvement, the cause of the taint has some other origin.

(Each wine producing country has its own list of permitted treatments and additives. The complete list of those permitted in Europe is to be found in Annex IV of Regulation (EEC) No 1493/1999 and the subsequent amendments, available from HM Stationery Office bookshops.)

Chapter 12

QUALITY CONTROL AND ANALYSIS

Wine has two defects: if you add water to it, you ruin it; if you do not add water, it ruins you.

Spanish Proverb

Analysis plays an essential part in the overall control of the quality of wine, but quality control is much broader than mere analysis. Quality control should be the responsibility of everybody who has any input to the creation of the final product. In the case of wine, the responsibility lies with the person who tends the vines, the people who pick the grapes, the tractor driver, the press operator, the winemaker, the filling machine operator, the packer, the warehousemen and anyone else through whose hands the wine passes. In other words, everyone who is involved with the winemaking process. They all play their part in safeguarding the quality of the wine.

Laboratory analysis is the means by which the necessary controls and processes can be selected and applied. Analytical methods are available for all the important components of wine and range from the simplest methods that can be operated in a corner of the winery to those requiring a research-style laboratory, with gas chromatograph, atomic absorption spectrometer, etc. The modern laboratory can be fully automated, producing results which are fed directly into a computer, even controlling the process by a feed-back loop. A good winery must have properly defined quality control procedures, one of which should be a regime of analysis, taking due note of the requirements of consumer countries.

Quality plan

A scheme of analysis should be developed that produces useful and meaningful results, not simply those analyses that are easy to perform. A well-designed analytical scheme plays a large part in the production of healthy wine with a good shelf-life. There is little point in filling books or computer spreadsheets with numerous data that serve no purpose.

From the time that grapes are being studied for approaching maturity, a regime of analysis should be devised, so that all the important parameters are tested at the appropriate moment. This plan should extend throughout the processing of the grapes, through the production of must and the transformation into wine, to the storage in bulk and the final packaging into the ultimate container. And a good quality plan would not finish here: it would extend into post bottling studies of shelf-life and the analysis of any sub-standard returned bottles.

The recording of results is of the utmost importance to a winemaker, for it is only by the recording of all the facts that it becomes possible to determine the reasons for success or failure. By studying these facts it should be possible to achieve continuous improvement. In a well-designed scheme of analysis and recording, it should be possible to trace the history of a wine from the lot number on the bottle, back through the blending to the individual components, and possibly even to the grapes from which each component was made. This not only gives useful information for the purposes of continual improvement, but also gives good protection in any case of complaint or investigation. In short, it is nothing more than common sense, and yet some wineries entrenched in their old ways cannot see the logic in this approach!

Records should be an integral part of the quality plan and should follow the passage of the grape through to its sale in bottle. These should be designed in such a way that immediate retrieval is possible. They can range from the simplest set of tables kept in books or files, to the most sophisticated computer based records, where complete traceability is possible at all levels.

When large-volume wine is purchased for sale as a branded wine of a constant style, a technical specification should be agreed with the supplier that encompasses all the parameters of importance, including the appropriate tolerance or range. Every shipment of the wine should be analysed to prove conformation to this specification.

TECHNICAL SPECIFICATION FOR WINE

WINE	Medium White VdT		**Ref. No**	99/815

ANALYSIS	UNITS	MINIMUM	IDEAL	MAXIMUM
Alcohol	% vol	11.0	11.5	12.0
Residual sugars	g/l	8	10	12
Total acidity (as tartaric)	g/l	7.0	7.5	8.0
Volatile acidity (as acetic)	g/l	–	–	0.6
Free sulphur dioxide	mg/l	35	40	45
Total sulphur dioxide	mg/l	–	–	260
Ascorbic acid	mg/l			
Sorbic acid	mg/l		nil	
Potassium	mg/l	–	–	1000
Calcium	mg/l	–	–	100
Sodium	mg/l	–	–	30
Iron	mg/l	2	–	10
Copper	mg/l	–	–	0.5
Carbon dioxide	mg/l	600	800	1000
Dissolved oxygen	mg/l	nil	nil	0.3
Filterability index	min/100	–	–	30
Micro-organisms	cols/ml	–	nil	100

Natural wine components

Alcoholic strength

Analysis of the alcoholic strength is important for two reasons. First, the price of table wine is linked in part to its alcoholic strength. A wine with an alcoholic strength of 11% vol will be more expensive than one at 10% vol, and it is important to know that the correct wine has been supplied. Second, all wines on sale in the EU must comply with the labelling regulations which allow a tolerance of only ±0.5% alcohol on the label declaration. It is therefore necessary to know that the declaration is legal.

One could add a third reason for wanting to know the alcoholic strength of a wine, for many consumers imagine that the quality of a wine is linked to its strength, often looking for the alcohol declaration before making the final decision to purchase. This is most unfortunate because, in reality, there is no connection between the two. The fact that Bordeaux Supérieur, for example, has a higher minimum alcoholic strength than simple Bordeaux does not necessarily mean that it is of higher quality. It is not the alcohol that enhances the quality, it is the extra concentration of the fruit elements in the juice that plays the important role; the higher alcohol is incidental.

The earliest known method of determining the strength of spirits was what was known as 'proving' the strength, hence the development of units of proof. The procedure was somewhat dramatic, involving wetting a small heap of gunpowder with the spirit and applying a lighted match. If the gunpowder ignited, the spirit was 'over proof'. If it would not burn then the spirit was 'under proof'. By experimenting with a range of strengths it was possible to calculate what became known as 'proof spirit', or 100° proof, and which actually contained about 57% alcohol by volume. A spirit of this strength would just allow the gunpowder to burn. The standard at which most spirits were sold was 70° proof, which is equivalent to the present day 40% alcohol. On the proof scale

100% ethanol registers 175°. This was all very confusing, particularly as the American proof was different, being precisely double the percentage by volume. Hence American spirits at 40% alcohol were labelled as 80° proof, giving the wrong impression that they were stronger than British spirits.

Thankfully, this confusion was swept away by Brussels when it declared that the unit of alcoholic strength would be the percentage by volume, abbreviated to % vol. It is worth noting that percentage by weight gives a considerably lower figure, due to the density of alcohol being much lower than that of water. A litre of water weighs 1.0000 kg, which, incidentally, is how a litre is defined, whereas a litre of pure ethanol weighs only 0.7897 kg.

Ethanol is surprisingly difficult to analyse by simple chemical methods because it is not very reactive, so most methods depend upon some physical characteristic, such as density or absorption of infra-red radiation, both of which lend themselves to automation.

The classical method, known as the distillation method, makes use of the large difference in density between water and alcohol. It involves boiling a sample of the wine, passing the vapours through a condenser, and collecting the liquid that condenses. This process separates the alcohol from most of the other components in the wine that might interfere by affecting the density. By measuring the density of the distillate, an accurate determination of the alcoholic strength can be made. Extensive tables are available giving the strength for every incremental change in density. This has been the official method for centuries, although it requires a great deal of expertise in the manipulation of the equipment if accurate results are to be obtained. Such is the esteem in which this method is held that only in 1997 was a modern instrumental method accepted as a reference method.

12.1 *Alcoholic strength by distillation*

Laboratories in wine producing countries, where hundreds of samples are measured every day, are usually equipped with automatic instruments, based on the measurement of the absorption of a beam of light in the near infra-red region (NIR) passing through the wine. A sample of wine is placed in the instrument, a button pressed, and the answer is printed out.

12.2 *Alcoholic strength by NIR absorption*

The methanol and the higher alcohols are easily measured by modern techniques. Being volatile (easily evaporated by heat), they lend themselves to gas chomatography (GC), one of the most widely used of analytical instruments and easily adapted to analyse any volatile substance. In this instrument, a small sample is injected into a long column containing an absorbent substance, and through which is passing a current of an inert gas. The column is heated in an oven, which vaporises the alcohols. The different properties of the various alcohols cause them to pass along the column at different speeds, resulting in a separation at the far end of the column. By arranging for them to pass through a suitable detector, the individual alcohols can be recorded separately by what is known as a chromatogram.

12.3 Chromatogram of alcohols in wine

Total acidity

The name of this parameter in the analysis of wines came about because it is a measure of all the acids in the wine, including the volatile acids (see below). An alternative name is titratable acidity, because the analysis is carried out by a titration. The results are the same, whatever the name, and even the commonly used abbreviation is the same for both.

Total acidity (TA) is determined by a simple titration, which will be familiar to all who studied chemistry at school. A pipette is used to measure a portion of wine into a conical flask, to which are added measured quantities of a standardised alkaline solution from a burette, until the resultant mixture is neutral. This moment in the titration, known as the end-point, can be detected by using an 'indicator', which is a substance that changes colour when the mixture in the flask becomes neutral. Nowadays, a pH meter (see below) is often used to detect the end-point, giving greater accuracy, especially with red wines, where a colour change may be difficult to see. The quantity of alkaline solution used is proportional to the total acidity of the wine.

12.4 Titration apparatus

The result has to be interpreted with care because it is not the measurement of a single acid, but is the sum of all the different acids present in the wine. The only way to obtain a meaningful result is to express it as if there were only one acid in the wine, and different countries have different traditions, which can cause confusion. The EU has adopted tartaric acid as the unit, which is logical, since this is the most abundant acid. The French still persist in expressing the results as sulphuric acid, which seems a rather strange unit to use, since it is hoped that their wines do not contain battery acid! The results yield a figure roughly half the size, conversion from sulphuric acid to tartaric acid requiring multiplication by 1.531.

The winemaker is interested in the total acidity at a very early stage, even prior to fermentation, for it is then that the first adjustment can be made. It is permissible, but less effective, to make a second adjustment after the fermentation. Thus, a titration for total acidity would be carried out at both of these moments during the production of the wine.

There is one legal aspect of total acidity that should be observed, which is that for table wines on sale within the EU, there should be a minimum of 4.5 g/litre, expressed as tartaric acid. (But wines as low as this will probably taste somewhat 'flabby' in any case.)

TA is one of those analyses that tend to be carried out because of its simplicity rather than its importance. Immediately prior to bottling there is little that can be done about total acidity. The important parameter is the taste: if the taste is correct, the wine is correct. There is, however, one very useful and unusual aspect of the measurement of total acidity that has been adopted by some bottling companies, which is a simple test for dilution and is used because of the ease of measurement. Total acidity is measured when the wine first arrives at the bottling plant, and is measured again in the first bottle from the bottling line. If the latter is lower than the former, this indicates that the wine must have been diluted by rinse water in the bottling line. The two results should be identical, and bottling should not commence until this situation has been achieved.

pH

For the non-scientist, pH is a somewhat difficult concept to come to terms with, being an indication of acidity, and yet not being the same as total acidity and whose figures are the opposite way round. With TA, the more acid the wine, the higher the figure, but with pH, the more acid the wine, the lower the figure.

The name pH comes from the French *pouvoir hydrogène*, meaning hydrogen power, and in scientific terms, pH is defined as the negative of the log to base 10 of the concentration of hydrogen ions, or pH = $-\log_{10}$ [H^+], a somewhat difficult concept to comprehend. However, for the purpose of winemaking, an understanding of the basic principles is all that is necessary. pH is expressed on a scale of 0 to 14, where 0 is very acidic (e.g. strong sulphuric acid), 14 is very alkaline (strong caustic soda) and 7 is neutral (as in pure water). Most wines fall in the range 2.8 to 4.0. A highly acidic Muscadet, for example, might be pH 2.9, whereas a soft warm climate red wine, such as Australian Merlot, might be pH 3.5. Although the range of pH found in wines is small, differences of 0.2 are important.

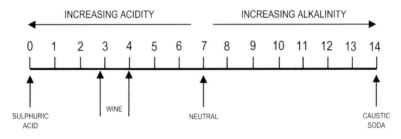

12.5 The full range of pH

Its relationship to total acidity is not straightforward, owing to what is known as the 'buffering' effect of the natural salts in the wine, which can cause a change in the pH without altering the total acidity. Thus, it is possible to have two wines of the same total acidity, yet with different pH, or vice versa. However, pH is the more important parameter, since this is the controlling function that affects colour, taste and keeping qualities, especially in relation to molecular sulphur dioxide (see p.131). It is probably best considered as an indication of the true acidity of the wine, as tasted in the mouth.

Measurement of pH is extremely simple by using a readily available and inexpensive piece of equipment known as a pH meter. All that is necessary is to dip the electrode into a sample of the wine and note the reading. Unfortunately, the electrode gradually changes and must be calibrated every day before use. This is also a simple operation using readily purchased tablets which, when dissolved in water, yield a solution of accurately known pH.

Volatile acidity

Volatile acidity (VA) is so-called because it is the component of total acidity that is volatile, meaning that it can be separated from the other acids by boiling the wine. The major constituent is acetic acid, the product of oxidation of alcohol.

The classical method of determining volatile acidity is to boil off the volatile acids in a simple glass still and collect them as a distillate, which is then titrated with alkali, as for total acidity. Because the volatile acidity is caused by a number of steam-volatile acids of different boiling points, the conditions of distillation must always be the same, including the design of the distillation apparatus, otherwise different results will be obtained. A second difficulty arises because of the formation of esters, which are not included in the titration as they are neutral and not acidic. Furthermore, if the acetic bacteria are active, the VA will constantly be changing. It is, therefore, sometimes difficult to get agreement between laboratories on the results of this determination.

As with total acidity, the result is expressed as if it were one acid, in this case acetic acid, the acid of vinegar and the most abundant acid. The French, however, continue to use sulphuric acid as the standard. To convert from sulphuric acid to acetic acid, the result must be multiplied by 1.225.

Residual sugars

Traditionally, the measurement of residual sugars in the laboratory is done by a Fehlings titration, which involves a reaction with copper salts. Although somewhat complex in terms of chemistry, the titration is simple, and gives a sufficiently accurate measure of the residual sugars in wine. Fehlings Solution, which is widely used in food laboratories, was invented by H C von Fehling, professor of chemistry at the polytechnic school at Stuttgart from 1839 to 1882.

A modern high technology laboratory will probably use high performance liquid chromatography (HPLC), in which the individual sugars are separated by passing the wine through a column of absorptive material, in a similar way to the separation of alcohols by gas chromatography. The various sugars pass through the column at different speeds, and thus appear at the detector at different times, producing peaks on a chromatogram that look somewhat similar to the results of gas chromatography, as above. All of this can be automated, with the results stored in a computer, ready for instant retrieval when needed. This is a very elegant and advanced form of analysis which gives a complete picture of the residual sugars in the wine and is of particular use in experimental production.

It is not possible to obtain a figure for the sugar content by measuring the density, as with musts before fermentation, because alcohol, being less dense than water, interferes with the density value. Similarly, the refractive index reading cannot be used because the refractive index of alcohol is different from that of water.

Tartrate stability tests

Although wine may have been refrigerated and should be tartrate stable, it is critically important to test the wine before bottling to ensure that stability has been achieved. The standard test for tartrate stability is to refrigerate a small sample at -4°C for three days and to examine the sample for traces of crystals. The presence of crystals at the end of the test indicates that the wine is unstable and that it should be treated further. If crystals are absent, it is unfortunately no guarantee that the wine is stable because colloids might be present which are preventing the deposition of crystals.

Tests that are more elaborate have been developed, one of which is based on the measurement of the concentration of all the substances in the wine that affect tartrate stability, viz. potassium, calcium, tartaric acid, alcohol and pH. After these have been measured, the results are entered into a formula which indicates whether the wine is stable or unstable.

Another test, which seems to be the most effective and practical, makes use of the change in electrical conductivity which takes place when there is a change in the concentration of dissolved salts in the wine: the stronger the solution, the greater the conductivity. In this test the wine is stirred at zero degrees with finely divided potassium bi-tartrate crystals and the change in electrical conductivity is measured. A rise in conductivity indicates that crystals are dissolving, showing that the wine is not saturated with tartrates and therefore should be stable. If the conductivity goes down, this indicates that tartrates are crystallising out, showing the wine to be supersaturated and thus unstable. Although better than the more simple tests, the most reliable results are produced with wines that are well known to the technician, because each wine has its own characteristics. In other words, this test works best for producers, who know their wines well, rather than bottlers, who have to handle large numbers of wine, all of which are different and have somewhat unknown properties.

Nevertheless, all of these tests fail from time to time because of the complex structure of wine, with its many colloidal substances, all of which interfere with normal crystallisation processes. In view of the unreliability of this entire subject, one might think that it would be easier to teach consumers to accept tartrate crystals!

Protein stability tests

Unstable proteins that cause potential problems of haze, cloudiness or deposit are easy to detect by submitting a small sample to abuse by heating it to 80°C and cooling it to -4°C. If it remains clear and bright, it is stable. If it produces a haze, or deposit, the wine needs fining. This test is an excellent example of an empirical quality control test, where extreme conditions are simulated in the laboratory and whose results indicate the treatment that is necessary.

It is also possible to detect unstable proteins by adding a solution of phosphomolybdic acid, widely available as the proprietary Bentotest reagent, that produces an immediate coagulation of the proteins, resulting in a visible haze. This can be a useful test, but tends to be over-sensitive, resulting in unnecessary treatment of the wine. As with the tartrate stability test, interpretation of the results is at its most reliable when applied to winemaking, where the characteristic behaviour of the wine is well known.

Chemical additives

Free sulphur dioxide

Checking for the correct level of free sulphur dioxide is the most frequently performed test in the quality control regime, because the protective action of sulphur dioxide is self-destructive. When oxygen dissolves in wine, the sulphur dioxide should destroy the free oxygen by reacting with it before it has a chance to oxidise any of the wine components. During this reaction the sulphur dioxide is itself destroyed by being converted to sulphuric acid (in minute quantity). At every stage in the wine making and handling process, further additions have to be made to keep the sulphur dioxide at the correct level.

Fortunately, the standard test is simple to perform and can be carried out on a table in a corner of the winery. It is possible to purchase a small kit of glassware and solutions from many laboratory suppliers to enable a titration to be performed in which a standard solution of potassium iodate, or iodine, is used to oxidise the sulphur dioxide, giving a direct reading of the free sulphur dioxide content of the wine.

The disadvantage of this simple method is that iodine is a reactive chemical and will oxidise other substances in the wine as well as sulphur dioxide. This is a particular drawback when the wine contains ascorbic acid, since iodine reacts with it as if it were sulphur dioxide. For results that are more accurate, a so-called 'blank' titration has to be carried out, by first adding acetaldehyde to a second sample of the wine. This binds up the entire free sulphur dioxide before the iodine titration is carried out. The result is the totality of all the other substances in the wine that will react with sulphur dioxide, and this 'blank' figure has to be subtracted from the first titration before calculating the result.

3. SULPHUR DIOXIDE IS
CARRIED ON AIR STREAM

1. AIR IS
PUMPED OUT

2. AIR IS
DRAWN IN

4. SULPHUR DIOXIDE
CAN BE TITRATED

12.6 Sulphur dioxide by aspiration

The only way of obtaining a truly accurate result is by using the official EU reference method, variously called the peroxide method, or the aspiration method, aspiration meaning drawing something through by suction. In this case a current of air is slowly bubbled through a sample of the wine in a special aspiration apparatus, as shown in diagram 12.6, carrying with it the free sulphur dioxide and leaving behind the non-volatile interfering substances. The current of air bearing the sulphur dioxide is then passed through a solution of hydrogen peroxide, which oxidises the sulphur dioxide to sulphuric acid. The sulphuric acid can then be titrated with a standard solution of sodium hydroxide.

Total sulphur dioxide

The same kit can be used for measuring the total sulphur dioxide by first treating the wine sample with an alkaline solution, which has the effect of releasing the bound sulphur dioxide and converting it to the free form. By performing a titration after this treatment, the total sulphur dioxide can be obtained. As it is the total sulphur dioxide that is controlled by EU regulation, it is important that this level is known every time before any additions are made, to ensure that the wine is kept within the legal limits.

The same caveat applies to the measurement of total sulphur dioxide as it does to the measurement of free sulphur dioxide: the simple iodine titration is prone to give falsely high results because of interference by other substances in the wine. With total sulphur dioxide subject to legal limits, in any case of litigation, the analysis must be performed by the aspiration method.

Other additives

Simple analytical methods are available for ascorbic acid and sorbic acid. As there are legal limits for both of these substances, analysis should always take place after any additions have been made, to ensure that the limit has not been exceeded.

Methods for the analysis of metatartaric acid and citric acid are more complex and are used only in those special cases where it is considered necessary for purposes of verification of legality, both of these additives also having legal limits imposed by EU regulations.

The addition of any permitted additive must always be accompanied by a subsequent analysis, to ensure that the correct level has been added. Despite the best controls in the most modern of wineries, it is not unknown for additions to be made twice, or for two operatives to assume that the other has made the addition, when neither has; hence the importance of keeping good records.

Contaminants

Dissolved oxygen

Oxygen will dissolve very readily in wine that is in contact with air, and once dissolved, the oxygen begins its steady task of destroying the wine. Unfortunately, the sulphur dioxide that is present in the wine does not react immediately with the oxygen, but co-exists with it for sufficient time to cause damage. Hence, the only safe practice is to prevent any dissolution of oxygen, and to monitor constantly the level of dissolved oxygen in the wine.

At normal room temperature, wine can absorb about 8 milligrams per litre of oxygen before becoming saturated. In a tank of wine, filled to the brim and properly sealed, this will gradually fall below 1 milligram per litre after about ten days, due to the scavenging effect of the sulphur dioxide. Every time the wine is moved, more oxygen dissolves, and this should be measured and monitored, so that techniques can be improved to minimise contact with oxygen.

At low temperatures, the dissolution of oxygen is increased, because oxygen becomes more soluble. Wine at -5°C can dissolve almost twice as much oxygen as at 20°C. Therefore, wine that has been chilled must be handled with even greater care than when it is at room temperature.

Dissolved oxygen is an analysis that can be performed very simply by using a meter designed specifically for the measurement of dissolved oxygen. In common with many of these electronic devices, the operation of such a meter is simple, but false results can easily be produced. First, the electrode tends to go out of calibration rather quickly, so requires constant checking. Second, because we are surrounded by an atmosphere containing 20% oxygen, care has to be taken to prevent high results.

Looking something like the ubiquitous pH meter, the dissolved oxygen meter has an electrode which is dipped into the wine and which gives a direct reading. Measurements should be taken after all stages of treatment and movement of wine, and all sources of dissolved oxygen should be eliminated. (See p.24 for further information.)

Iron and copper

Although both of these elements occur naturally in all grape juice and wine, an excessive level indicates that contamination has occurred. An iron concentration above the natural level of around 10 mg/litre indicates the use of old galvanised buckets or ancient presses with bare iron components. Copper levels are normally much lower, being less than 0.2 mg/litre. An elevated copper content is usually caused by bronze fittings or pumps in the winery, or late spraying of copper fungicides in the vineyard. Both elements are undesirable in excess because they are the cause of both casse and oxidation.

Paradoxically, a small quantity of copper is desirable in wine, acting as a cleansing agent and removing traces of hydrogen sulphide (H_2S), the cause of the 'bad egg' smell that sometimes becomes apparent when sulphur dioxide is reduced. This phenomenon occurs more frequently now that copper and bronze equipment has been removed from wineries and everything is made of inert stainless steel. Winemakers sometimes actually have to add a small quantity of copper sulphate to precipitate the sulphide as the very insoluble copper sulphide.

It is interesting to note that in very old-fashioned wineries, where even the pipework is made of copper, the wine is not heavily contaminated. The inner surfaces become covered with black copper sulphide, which forms an inert coating, preventing the copper dissolving.

In the days of classical analysis, determination of iron and copper was tedious and difficult. Nowadays, it is made simple with modern instrumental equipment, such as an atomic absorption spectrometer (AA). A beam of light from a special lamp with electrodes made from the element being determined is passed through a gas flame.

The wine is sprayed into the flame in the form of a fine mist, and the change in the intensity of the beam is measured. This gives a very specific and accurate way of checking the concentration of different metals in the wine; all that is needed is a separate lamp for each element.

12.7 Determination of metals by atomic absorption

Sodium

Wines are naturally rich in potassium and very low in sodium, normal levels being 1000 mg/litre and 20 mg/litre respectively. Ion exchange alters this ratio considerably, a change that is particularly noticeable in the sodium concentration, which can be raised by a factor of ten. Thus, measurement of the sodium content of a wine is a simple test for ion exchange. This is easily carried out with equipment such as a flame photometer, which measures the emission of light at the characteristic sodium wavelength, the yellow light with which we are all familiar in the form of street lighting.

Microbiological analysis

The yeasts and bacteria that play an important role in the production of wine are unwelcome entities when the time comes to put the wine into a bottle. In high quality traditionally made wines, their presence is of no great importance, because, in the absence of air, the bacteria cannot survive, and the yeasts will quickly die, if not already dead, due to lack of nutrients.

The situation with wines containing residual sugar is, however, quite different. If these wines still contain viable yeast cells when bottled, a second fermentation will start in the bottle, with disastrous results, hence the importance not only of a good technique of aseptic bottling, but a reliable procedure for checking for the absence of micro-organisms.

A remarkably simple and elegant test has been developed, which is widely used and requires no expensive equipment, neither microscope nor a sterile room. All that is necessary is a specially designed funnel which will hold a small circular piece of membrane filter in the base, a flask into which the funnel fits, and a vacuum pump.

Before commencing the test the funnel is sterilised either by steaming or by covering with alcohol and burning it off. The membrane filter is purchased already sterilised and is fitted to the funnel and the funnel placed in the flask. The wine sample is poured into the funnel, the vacuum pump turned on and the wine is sucked through the membrane, leaving any micro-organisms stranded on the surface of the membrane.

The membrane is then removed from the funnel and placed on the surface of a nutrient medium in a sterile petri dish. The nutrient diffuses into the pores of the membrane and nourishes any living cells that might be present, which reproduce rapidly. After three days each cell grows into such a large colony that it can be seen with the naked eye. All that is necessary is to examine the membrane and count any colonies that might be visible. A successful bottling is indicated by a membrane that is as clean as when it was first removed from its packet.

The photographs at 12.8 and 12.9 are tests from a dirty and a clean wine respectively. In 12.8 the creamy coloured compact spots are yeast colonies, each of which started as a single yeast cell, which has multiplied thousands of times to become a colony visible to the naked eye. The flatter and broader growth near the seven o'clock

1 2.8 A contaminated wine   *12.9 A good micro test result*

position is a bacterial colony, and the fluffy areas are colonies of mould, indicating a distinctly bad bottling where the wine is highly contaminated with various micro-organisms. The result shown at 12.9 is the norm for a well-managed modern bottling line.

12.10 Photomicrograph of a yeast colony

The picture above shows the colony of yeast that has developed in only three days from a single cell of *Saccharomyces cerevisiae,* hence the need for high standards of hygiene in all wineries.

Chapter 13

STORAGE AND MATURATION

I love everything that is old; old friends, old times, old manners, old books, old wines.

Oliver Goldsmith 1726-1774

Wine spends much of its life waiting; it is not constantly being treated, or analysed, or being moved or blended. Much of the time it is sitting in a vat or a barrel or a bottle, waiting for things to happen. During each of these periods something different is occurring, according to the container it is in, and according to the wishes of the winemaker. The important parameter in all of these situations is the control of oxygen.

Storage without change

If wine which is still in bulk is required to remain unchanged for many months, oxygen must be totally excluded. This is best achieved by the use of stainless steel vats, kept brim-full. Concrete vats would be equally good, provided they are lined either with epoxy resin or with tiles in good condition, as would epoxy-lined or enamelled mild steel vats. This is the storage method of choice for high-volume branded wines, whose character should not change from the beginning to the end of each year and from one vintage to the next.

13.1 Stainless steel vats

Ideally, wine should be stored in the largest available vat, provided there is sufficient wine to fill the vat to the brim. An interesting phenomenon, known as the 'surface effect', which applies to any container, from vat to bottle, is that the smaller the container, the greater the change in the contents over a given period. This is because chemical changes occur at the interface between the liquid and the surface of the container, and the smaller the container the greater the ratio of surface to volume.

Vats come in all shapes and sizes, from 25 hl (2500 litres) up to 500 hl (50,000 litres) and possibly even bigger. If it is not possible to keep the vats brim-full, the headspace must be oxygen-free; the air must be replaced with an inert gas, preferably nitrogen, which does not dissolve in the wine. Carbon dioxide, being heavier than air, is very good for sweeping the air out of empty vats, but it has the disadvantage of being soluble in wine. If left above the surface of wine, it gradually dissolves, especially if the wine is cold, letting air into the headspace of the vat. Conversely, if wine is kept under pure nitrogen for a long time, the residual carbon dioxide in the wine, which gives it a 'lively' taste, is lost and the wine becomes somewhat flat. The ideal gas for blanketing purposes is a mixture of nitrogen and carbon dioxide, the proportions depending on the desired carbon dioxide content of the wine (see p.95 for further information).

Because of the constant loss of sulphur dioxide as it does its work, analysis of the free sulphur dioxide level must take place after every movement and every treatment, and weekly during storage, with appropriate additions as necessary.

Maturation in wood

Maturation in wood is used for an entirely different purpose compared with storage in stainless steel, and is used primarily for **red wines** after they have finished their fermentation in tanks and have been separated from the skins. Wood is deliberately chosen to promote slow oxidation, which changes the nature of the wine. The source of the oxygen is two-fold, the first being the air that diffuses inwards through the pores in the wood and the second the air that becomes dissolved in the wine during racking.

13.2 Wine maturing in barriques

The main changes that take place are the oxidation and polymerisation (joining together of the molecules) of the polyphenols, principally the harsh tannin constituents. These gradually form an insoluble substance that falls to the bottom of the barrels, leaving the wine softer and more harmonious. At the same time, wood tannins are extracted into the wine, giving more complexity, especially with the added flavour of vanillin. This is emphasised by the toasting that the interior of the barrel receives from the fire used to soften the staves during its construction. In fact, the degree of toasting is one of the variables that appears to be fashionable at present.

The rate at which the maturation occurs depends upon several factors:

- Type of woodwood: oak is the usual wood of choice for barrel ageing, as it adds flavour as well as providing the right environment for oxidation. Different oaks can be used, including American, Hungarian, and from France, Limousin, Tronçais,

Alliers, and Nevers, all of which influence the result in different ways. American oak is of a different variety from the European sources and has larger pores, giving a more rapid maturation, as well as adding more flavour.

- size of barrel: the smaller the barrel, the quicker the maturation because the smaller the container, the greater the surface to volume ratio and therefore the greater the proportion of air coming in through the pores of the wood.

- Age of barrel: in older barrels the pores become partially blocked by deposits from previous wines, so diffusion of air is slower. New oak also has a ready supply of oak tannins and vanillins, which are extracted by the wine, adding to its flavour. Care is needed when using new barrels because the oak flavour can easily dominate the fruit and produce an unbalanced wine. Many top class estates use new oak barrels for each vintage, but the wine is transferred to second year barrels after six to eight months, to prevent over-extraction of oak flavour.

- Frequency of racking: more frequent racking results in a greater dissolution of air.

- Temperature of cellar: chemical reactions proceed faster under warmer conditions.

The art of barrel maturation is knowing the correct combination of all the above factors, which can only be learned by trial and error, and perfected by long experience.

It is equally important, and more of a chore than an art, to take great care of wines when they are spending their sojourn in wood. It is all too easy to neglect them and leave them to nature. As any gardener knows, leaving things to nature does not work: nature needs help. Barrels must be racked from time to time, to remove the sediment which, if left in contact with the wine, can impart unpleasant off-flavours. Barrels must be topped-up regularly, to prevent excessive oxidation, and must be turned to the right position (the 'two o'clock position') to keep the bung wet.

The situation with **white wines** is somewhat different, in that the fermentation can be carried out in the barrel, which has a complex and subtle effect on the character of the wine (see p.82). Despite the advantages that this practice can offer, many white wines are transferred to barrels after the fermentation has been completed simply to obtain the oak flavours.

Unfortunately, oak barrels are an expensive commodity, and sometimes old barrels and vats are kept in use far too long, a practice which can lead to tainted wine, especially if the vats are not scraped and cleaned properly.

A much cheaper way of using oak is to put the wood into the wine, rather than the wine into wood, or in other words using oak chips or staves immersed in the wine. This is a relatively cheap way of obtaining the oak flavours, but does not give the subtlety of barrel maturation. Great care and expertise is needed during this process, for it is very easy to overdo the oak influence, resulting in a wine that is totally out of balance and tasting of wood extract rather than grape.

An even more dubious method of obtaining 'oak influence' is the use of oak essence, a practice which is officially not permitted in Europe, but almost certainly does occur. The proximity of essence factories to producers of famous oak-influenced wines has been noted.

Many winemakers are obsessed with the use of oak and are experimenting with its use in areas where it was traditionally absent. This is a pity, as it changes the character of wines which already have their own unique style obtained solely from the grape. It is not necessary to have added vanillin in order to be great. Individuality is a valuable asset and should be treasured and not lost in the name of fashion.

Maturation in bottle

The final stage of maturation, bottle ageing, is a distinctly separate phase in the maturation process in that the conditions are anaerobic: oxygen does not have a part to play. The old idea that the natural cork in the bottle transmits the perfect amount of oxygen to aid maturation is debatable, as is the concept that cork plays a positive role in the maturation process. The reactions taking place are purely chemical reactions between constituents of the wine, largely between alcohols, acids and water. Alcohols and acids form esters, which in turn are broken down by water to alcohols and acids, which then inter-react producing yet more esters, and so on.

$$CH_3CO\,\underline{OH} \ + \ H\,\underline{OCH_2CH_3} \ \rightarrow \ CH_3COOCH_2CH_3 \ + H_2O$$

acetic acid   ethanol   ethyl acetate   water

Over 500 different compounds have been identified in the aroma of a mature red wine. These include alcohols, volatile acids, esters, aldehydes, ketones and all the products of interaction, decomposition and hydrolysis (their reaction with water).

13.3 Wine maturing in bottles

The 'surface effect' as described above has a big influence on the rate of maturation in bottle, which explains why magnums mature slowly, while half-bottles reach their peak fairly quickly. The ultimately better wine in a magnum is undoubtedly due to the slower rate of chemical reaction of the constituents, which gives more opportunity for inter-reactions to take place. This results in a greater variety of chemical compounds and, hence, a greater complexity.

During this period of anaerobic maturation, the wine needs to rest under constant conditions. Rapid changes in temperature upset the slow process of chemical inter-reactions; light, and especially UV radiation, speeds up the decomposition of the sensitive components; vibration prevents the settling of the fine deposits that are produced. All of these phenomena confirm that the tradition of keeping bottled wine in a cool, dark, dry cellar is important if the best results are to be obtained.

However, there is no need to despair if such a cellar is not available for a personal collection of wine. All that is necessary for reasonable storage is darkness and a temperature that does not fluctuate violently: the actual temperature is less important, but the cooler the better. A cupboard under the stairs might suffice, or alternatively, a solidly built cupboard at the back of the garage. The worst conditions would be in a loft that gets hot during the day, and dips down towards freezing each night.

Chapter 14

PACKAGING AND BOTTLING

Neither do you put new wine into old wine-skins; if you do, the skins burst, and then the wine runs out and the skins are spoilt.

Matthew 9 17

Wine is ready for bottling only when it has been fully analysed, and all the necessary treatments and corrections have been completed. Failure to prepare the wine properly can result in a short shelf life, or possibly even the development of faults. A good system of quality control is a safeguard against the development of faulty wine. This has been demonstrated by the considerably reduced frequency of faulty bottles during the last decade or so.

Packaging materials

There is a wealth of choice in the way wine is packed nowadays. Traditions have been slow to break, but no longer are we bound to purchase wine in a glass bottle, closed by a piece of natural cork. However, the techniques required for packaging in the various formats demand specialist knowledge because each has its own specific requirements.

Glass bottles

Irrespective of tradition, the glass bottle is probably the best container for wine that has yet been invented. It is inert and has no possibilities for taint; it is impermeable to gases, and is available in almost any shape and size. Set against this is the fact that it is fragile, heavy and is transparent to UV radiation, which is a particular danger in supermarkets, where bottles are sometimes displayed close to fluorescent lights.

The techniques of glass manufacture have improved enormously, due largely to the effects of the quality revolution that has taken place throughout manufacturing industry, where it is realised that quality is important and that quality sells product. Glass bottles purchased direct from the glassworks are supplied by the pallet, tightly wrapped in polythene and are virtually sterile, having been palletised whilst still hot. The quality of bottles is better than ever before; even the cardboard layer pads between the layers on the pallets have been replaced with plastic to eliminate the possibility of contamination with fibres. It is a pity that many food technologists insist on bottles being rinsed with water before filling, as this can result in the bottles being contaminated unless the rinsing machine is immaculately serviced. If bottle rinsing machines have to be used, the rinse water should be fresh and not re-circulated, and should either be filtered through a 0.2m membrane or treated with sulphur dioxide or ozone to destroy any micro-organisms that might be present. The most meticulous operators do both.

Measuring container bottles

A revolution in filling control has taken place in Europe with the introduction of the measuring container bottle (MCB). This is a bottle whose capacity has been controlled during its manufacture in such a way that the filler of the bottle has only to measure the level of the liquid in the neck to guarantee that, on average, the bottle holds the declared quantity.

The EU Measuring Container legislation puts the onus on the bottle manufacturer to keep the internal volume of the bottles within set limits, at a stated level from the top of the bottle. This level is embossed on the side of the bottle near the base and appears as, for example, 63mm. The MCB style of bottle is recognised by a reversed epsilon, ꓱ, also embossed near the base of the bottle.

When using MCBs, all that is necessary for filling control is to measure the distance from the top of the bottle to the meniscus on a given number of bottles as they travel down the bottling line. The joy of this system is that the test is non-destructive and very simple. It is quite incorrect to empty bottles into a measuring cylinder because by doing this the useful MCB legislation is being ignored and the responsibility that belongs to the bottle manufacturer is being shouldered. Nevertheless, many bottlers are still doing it, especially in continental Europe. The reasoning offered (possibly justifiable) is that they are keeping a check on the bottle manufacturer.

Plastic bottles

It is important to distinguish two main types of plastic from which bottles are made: PVC (polyvinyl chloride) and PET (polyethylene terephthalate). PVC bottles are used widely in producer countries such as France, where wine is regarded as an everyday commodity. They are cheap and lightweight, but have virtually no barrier to gases; they let in the oxygen from the atmosphere, resulting in a short shelf life. This is perfectly acceptable for wines that are intended for rapid distribution and immediate consumption.

PET bottles are widely used for beers and soft drinks because they have better oxygen barrier properties and therefore offer a reasonable shelf life. However, the UK public has never taken to wine in plastic bottles and their sole use in the wine trade has been in the 18.75cl size. This quarter-bottle size is popular with airlines for in-flight consumption, where their light weight has proved an advantage. They can even be produced with a concave side to prevent them rolling off the food trays! However, for the dual reasons of their small size and a moderate oxygen barrier, the shelf life is only some three to six months. Stock control therefore becomes critical.

Aluminium cans

Market forces have dictated that the only size of aluminium can available for wine packaging is the 25cl, which makes a convenient two-glass size. The properties of the can are good: strong, lightweight, impermeable to light and to gases, easily filled with the elimination of both air and micro-organisms, and a shelf-life of about nine months, and all this with a lower than normal sulphur dioxide level.

The greatest technical problem that had to be solved was the fact that wine and aluminium do not make good companions. The acids in the wine attack aluminium and, in the process, the sulphur dioxide in the wine becomes reduced to hydrogen sulphide, or bad egg smell. This stretched lacquer technology to its limits, but success was achieved and wine in cans has proved to be viable. Their popularity, however, is not great; perhaps they are too small or the unit cost is too high, or maybe it is purely traditional resistance to anything that is not glass.

Bag-in-box

The purpose of this style of packaging is to provide a means of purchasing a large quantity of wine that can be drawn off a glass at a time over a long period, with minimum deterioration. The bag-in-box is available in 2 litre, 3 litre, 5 litre, 10 litre and even 20 litre sizes and is a useful means of buying larger quantities of wine. The technology of this form of packaging is complex and expensive, and it was never intended to be a cheap bulk pack.

It was invented in the USA during the 1970s, but was developed in Australia, where it became extremely popular, due to the low price (There was no wine duty in those days!) and the availability of large quantities of a good quality, everyday style of wine. It was also noted that the Australians possess large refrigerators in which they can keep the boxes.

The principle of drawing off a glass of wine at a time without deterioration has largely been achieved, although the total shelf life of the pack is still limited, being about nine months for a three litre box from the time of packing, irrespective of whether or not it has been broached. It is advisable to purchase bag-in-box wines only when needed, and from an outlet that has a good turnover and can guarantee fresh stock. The shelf life of the larger sizes is longer, because of the bigger volume to surface ratio, and they have proved to be a useful way of serving single glasses of wine in pubs and restaurants.

Inside the box there is a flexible bag, which collapses as the wine is drawn off so that air is kept away from the wine. The technology involved is considerable because the material of the bag has to be flexible and yet retain good barrier properties. The tap must not leak and must also prevent ingress of air; and the box must withstand the considerable hydraulic forces of litres of wine moving from side to side during transport.

The material of the bag has been the greatest technical problem, trying to combine flexibility with a good oxygen barrier. If the bag does not collapse readily, air bubbles in through the tap when wine is drawn off, which results in oxidation of the remaining wine. The obvious choice might seem to be the simple polythene bag, widely used for containing many foodstuffs: inert, non-toxic and easy to weld. Unfortunately, it is as transparent to oxygen as it is to light, and wine stored in a polythene bag will oxidise as rapidly as in an opened bottle. Most bag material nowadays is a complex structure consisting of two outer layers of high density polyethylene (HDPE) between which is sandwiched an oxygen barrier consisting of a film of polyester which has been coated with a layer of aluminium. Sometimes this barrier layer consists of a very thin sheet of aluminium foil, which gives excellent protection when new, but deteriorates when in use, due to minute cracks that appear in the foil when it is flexed (known as flex cracking).

Even those bags that look as if they might be made of simple polythene because they are transparent are concealing an equally complex structure. In this case the oxygen barrier is not aluminium but polyvinyl alcohol (PVA), a plastic that prevents the passage of oxygen. PVA does not suffer from flex-cracking, but does not have such a good initial oxygen barrier as aluminium foil. Therefore, the choice is between a better oxygen barrier with potential flex-cracking, and a poorer barrier but more robust.

Filling is also critical and must be more tightly controlled than for the filling of glass bottles. The flexible nature of the bag presents the first problem, for the total capacity of a bag intended for three litres is actually nearer to five if filled to the maximum. If not properly supported during filling, a large air bubble can be incorporated in the bag, which would be disastrous for its shelf life. The filling machines must be carefully designed and expertly operated to ensure that only the smallest air bubble is trapped in the bag.

The tap is another route by which oxygen can enter. A great deal of research has gone into the design of what looks like a very simple tap, which it is – ingeniously simple. The three basic requirements are that it must allow the wine to flow out quickly when operated, it must not leak when closed and it must not allow oxygen to enter the bag.

The highest standards of wine preparation and microbiological control are necessary. Despite the best efforts of the laminate technologists, the oxygen barrier has not been perfected, although it is greatly improved from the early days of bag-in-box. The resultant small amount of oxygen that gets into the bag encourages any yeasts to multiply. Hence, the microbiological standards for filling must be a total absence of all yeast and all bacteria, which is not difficult to achieve with modern methods of sterilisation and filtration.

When the wine is packed it is necessary to use a higher level of sulphur dioxide to combat the small ingress of oxygen. This has led to some criticism of the bag-in-box technique, but the sulphur dioxide falls to normal levels by the time the pack is on the retailer's shelves.

A further criticism has been that the quality of the wine in bag-in-box is lower than that in bottles. This was probably true in the early days, when packers of bag-in-box deliberately chose cheap wines to keep the price down. Nowadays there is a large range of good quality wine available in bag-in-box, with a good shelf-life. The improvement in the quality of the wine used brought with it an increased shelf-life, good wine naturally lasting longer than cheaply made wine.

Cardboard 'bricks'

Fruit juices and milk are frequently found packaged in what are generically known as 'cardboard bricks', as exemplified by the Tetra

Brik. This is an excellent form of packaging, of low cost, with a good oxygen barrier and a good shelf life. Supermarkets in continental Europe frequently stock the cheaper wines in this format, but it has never been widely accepted in the UK for wine, because of its image, despite its popularity for fruit juices and milk.

The idea is quite revolutionary and is best imagined as the package being formed around the wine, rather than the wine being put into a package. The structure of the packaging material is important, consisting of a laminate of polythene, cardboard, aluminium foil (the oxygen barrier) and another layer of polythene (to protect the aluminium). The material is delivered on a large reel, which is fed into the filling machine, where it is first formed into a tube, and the bottom sealed. The wine is piped into the tube from above, the tube is sealed and cut into correctly sized portions. The portions are squeezed into rectangular shape and the ears are bent down to produce the familiar brick shape.

Closures

The traditional closure for wine bottles has long been the **natural cork**. Time was when it was held that cork was the perfect closure, letting in the small quantities of oxygen that were necessary for the maturation process. Although this theory has been challenged by the proponents of other forms of closure, cork remains the closure of choice for all high quality wines.

Cork has characteristics that make it very useful as a bottle closure. It is cheap, readily available, comes from a renewable source, is biodegradable and is a good oxygen barrier. It is elastic, can be compressed, and will quickly regain its original size. It possesses an amazing anti-slip property, which holds it in place without undue force from the cork itself. Cork is composed of hollow cells containing air. When cut by the punching tool, the surface of the cork presents a series of sucker-like cups to the bottle neck, which holds the cork in place and yet enables it to be removed by applying a gentle force.

The problem of cork taint has resulted in a decrease in the popularity of natural cork, with many bottlers searching for an alternative closure. Having been heavily criticised for an apparent increase in this problem, the cork industry rallied by way of an extensive project, code-named Quercus, by which it admitted to the problem and undertook to take wide-ranging steps towards its long-term cure. It was confirmed that the prime cause of the taint was a reaction between a penicillium mould in the crevices of the cork and the chlorine-containing chemicals used in the sterilising process. This reaction produced trichloranisole (TCA), a substance with a powerful fungal aroma.

In 1996 the European Cork Federation introduced a new Code of Good Manufacturing Practice for Cork which contains various recommendations for improvement. These include careful harvesting of the cork bark, storage off the ground and a replacement of the chlorine process by one based on peroxide which eliminates the precursor to the TCA. This should result in a considerable fall in the incidence of cork taint, but it is unfortunate that cork has acquired a bad image and the cork industry has been slow in responding.

The other fact about cork that has led to a reduction in its use is that producers and bottlers have been trading down under pressure from the large retailers, and have been using corks of lower grade and smaller size. Both of these factors increase the incidence of faulty bottles, poorer quality corks giving poorer seals. Hopefully, with an increased awareness of the potential quality of good natural cork, the situation will improve, and cork will regain its position as the closure of choice.

The closure with the best oxygen barrier is the **metal screw cap**, which gives a perfect seal every time, provided the capping machine is correctly adjusted. The thread on the caps is formed within the capping machine, and one that is badly adjusted produces caps that refuse to unscrew. On the positive side, they do not cause taint, do not suffer from quality variation and do not need a special tool for opening. Trials conducted some twenty years ago showed that the metal cap provides the best means of closure for glass bottles. Unfortunately they do not have a quality image and are associated with cheap products.

A vast amount of research has gone into the production of an artificial replacement for the cork. The **plastic stopper** is made from a type of plastic foam, and has proved to be very controversial. The early versions were difficult to apply, causing damage to corking machines, and were equally difficult to remove from the bottle. Some would claim that traces of chemicals enter the wine from the plastic, and that the plastic itself absorbs flavour components from the wine. There are those who would say that it is a pointless product – it is trying to imitate natural cork, which itself has imperfections. So, what are the facts? The truth is that it is a new product, scientific facts are in short supply, and emotions run high.

One cannot help wondering why manufacturers should bother with the production of such a closure. The answer is simple: everyone likes the ceremonial of the extraction of the cork, with its accompanying "plop!" There can be do doubt that it will not taint the wine with TCA – and it is available in a range of bright colours. Only time will tell whether it proves to be a successful and acceptable alternative to natural cork.

Capsules

The traditional capsule was developed from the practice of protecting the exposed end of the cork to prevent it from drying out. The earliest way of doing this was to dip the neck of the bottle in sealing wax, a practice that is still occasionally seen, if only as a marketing gimmick.

The first capsules were made of **lead foil** which served the dual purpose of keeping the top of the cork from drying out and, due to the toxic nature of lead salts, of killing any cork weevils that might try to enter. With the increase in scientific knowledge, it was realised that this practice might also have a detrimental effect on the drinker if the wine became heavily contaminated with lead.

So the lead was replaced with what was known as the **tin-lead capsule**, a sandwich of lead between two layers of tin, an attempt to keep the cost of the capsule down, tin being very expensive. This material stayed in use for many years, until it was realised that the outer tin layers were usually imperfect, allowing wine access to the lead in the middle of the sandwich, resulting again in the production of lead salts. After a major research programme by the UK Ministry of Agriculture, Fisheries and Food (MAFF), it was discovered that the first glass poured from a bottle whose neck was encrusted with lead salts contained sufficient lead for it to be rendered a toxic drink. As a result of this research, all capsules made from any material containing lead were banned by the entire EU as from 1993 (except on wines bottled prior to this date).

The material that gives the best appearance, but is also the most expensive, is **pure tin**, which is malleable and easily moulded to the neck of the bottle. The appearance is high class, it cuts easily for opening, and it is non-toxic.

The only other metal capsule that is acceptable is that which is made from **aluminium**. This metal is not as malleable as tin, and requires careful application if creases are to be avoided, but it is cheaper.

The most widely used material on everyday wines is **plastic**, which is available in a wide range of colours and finishes, and presents a very acceptable appearance, indistinguishable from expensive tin – until the time comes for opening. These capsules are made from an ingeniously produced plastic that has been stretched in one direction during manufacture. After applying the capsule to the bottle, it passes through a heat tunnel, where the plastic is softened and thereby shrinks back to its natural size, giving an excellent fit to the bottle neck.

Bottling processes

Bottling wine without any microbiological precautions is totally satisfactory for those wines whose fermentation has ceased naturally after most of the sugars have been consumed; but this will not work for wines containing residual fermentable sugars. With the advent of modern technology it has become possible to stop the fermentation at will, before the natural end of the fermentation. Such wines are unstable and will go into a second fermentation the instant a stray yeast enters the wine. Further, to satisfy the demand for medium dry wines, unfermented grape juice is frequently added during the final blending process, making the wine even more attractive to yeasts. The only way such unstable wines can be bottled is by the use of aseptic bottling techniques. These techniques have become the norm in many modern wineries, where all wines are bottled aseptically, even when it is not necessary. It could be said that technicians have had too strong an influence on the bottling process, demanding levels of sterility that are quite unnecessary and possibly even detrimental to the quality of the wine. As always, minimum treatment should be the rule.

This type of bottling is often referred to as sterile bottling, which is not strictly correct because sterile means the total absence of micro-organisms. This is not true of wine bottling because no attempt is made to eliminate all micro-organisms. Indeed, it is not necessary to go to such lengths, even with the most delicate of wines. The correct description, aseptic, which means the prevention of putrefaction, in wine technology terms means the removal of the yeasts and bacteria which cause re-fermentation or volatile acidity.

Yeasts and bacteria can be eliminated either by heating the wine, which kills them, or by filtration, which physically removes them. Heat can damage wine, so it needs to be applied carefully, with knowledge and with strict quality control procedures, and of course, heating involves energy and energy is expensive.

There are three principle ways in which heat can be used, with different combinations of time and temperature: a high temperature for a very short time, as in flash pasteurisation, a medium temperature for a medium length of time, as in tunnel pasteurisation, or a low temperature for a long time, as in thermotic bottling.

All of these methods are controversial because there is one school of opinion that insists that any form of heat applied to wine is damaging.

Despite any emotive arguments about heating wine, from a scientific point of view it is accepted that heat will affect the way a wine matures because reactions proceed more quickly at elevated temperatures. Maturation is all about chemical reactions between the constituents of the wine. However, this is all a matter of opinion, and very controversial. There is a well known and highly respected producer in Burgundy who flash pasteurises all his red wines, simply because he considers that, for his wines, this gives the best result and is preferable to filtration. (The technical advisor to the founder of the company was Louis Pasteur, so it is hardly surprising that the company still uses pasteurisation!)

The traditional, or non-aseptic, method

Long before aseptic techniques were even heard of, wine has been bottled without any form of treatment. Given time, and a good winemaker, wine is naturally self-clarifying and can be bottled without fining or filtration, provided it has been completely fermented out and the cork is sound. The wine will come to no harm because the yeast will die out, the alcohol will prevent the growth of any harmful organism, and the acetobacter will have no effect due to the absence of oxygen. There could be the occasional attack from other bacterial infections, and a porous cork might allow volatile acidity to develop, but, by and large, the wine will be able to mature in the bottle to complete satisfaction. It is becoming fashionable to offer such wines for sale, when they are given fancy titles such as 'Cuvée non-filtre'.

In this method of minimalist technology, the wine is fined, if necessary, racked to render it bright, and then bottled with no further treatment. It is quite likely that some deposit will form in the bottle after a few weeks or months, but this will probably not matter to the type of consumer that is likely to drink this style of wine and is familiar with decanting vintage port and fine claret.

Thermotic, or Hot Bottling

This method of aseptic bottling makes use of the lowest level of heat, with the longest cooling time. The wine is heated before going to the filling machine by passing it through a heat exchanger, which heats it just sufficiently to bring the temperature to 54°C. This is far below sterilising temperature, the standard conditions for which are 82°C for at least 20 minutes, conditions which are used, for example, for the sterilisation of hospital instruments. It is bottled at 54°C, corked, packed into cases and put away in the warehouse, where it slowly cools to ambient temperature. The yeast and bacteria are killed by virtue of the long period at elevated temperature, rather than the temperature itself.

In the early days of this technology, it was said that this method damaged the wine because of the effect of the heat. This was probably true in some cases, and, indeed, one almost expected the cheap one-and-a-half litre with the screw cap to taste as if it had been used for boiling cabbages. But times have changed, and with good temperature control, and it has to be very good with a variation as small as 0.2° either side of 54°C, this method produces results possibly even better for some wines than by cold filling methods. This is especially true of young, simple wines, where the small degree of heat advances the maturity slightly, giving the wine a softer and rounder character.

One great advantage of this method is that the contents of the bottle are sterilised after filling and after the bottle has been closed with the cork or the cap. Any yeasts or bacteria that are present in the wine or on the bottles or corks will be killed. The benefit that this offers is that it is not necessary for the operators on the bottling line to adopt sterile techniques when the wine is being bottled. On the other hand, it does not give *carte blanche* for operating to low standards. It is still necessary to ensure that the microbiological loading is low because none of the methods involving heat can cope with large numbers of micro-organisms. And, after all, wine is a foodstuff, and all foodstuffs should be handled with the correct degree of hygiene.

The one practical problem that has to be overcome is the control of filling level. If the wine is adjusted to the correct filling level when hot, it will be under-filled when at room temperature. Allowance has to be made, therefore, for the contraction of wine when filling takes place at an elevated temperature.

Tunnel pasteurisation

Louis Pasteur, the great French microbiologist, discovered that heat treatment slowed the deterioration of both milk and wine. The process of pasteurisation has been adapted in two forms for the bottling of wine. The earlier of the two processes, known as tunnel pasteurisation, involves heating the wine in the bottle, after bottling and capping. Like thermotic bottling above, this process has the benefit of requiring only good hygiene during its operation, not sterile techniques, all the organisms being killed in the closed bottle.

14.1 A pasteurising tunnel

The difference from thermotic bottling is that for tunnel pasteurisation the wine is bottled cold and the bottles of cold wine are passed slowly through a large heat tunnel where the contents are raised to 82°C for about fifteen minutes by passing through sprays of hot water. Compared with thermotic bottling, a higher temperature is used, but for a shorter time. At the end of the tunnel the bottles pass through cold water sprays, which bring the temperature of the wine quickly down to room temperature before any damage can be done, the whole cycle taking about forty-five minutes.

14.2 Bottles inside a tunnel pasteuriser

The equipment is expensive to install because it involves the installation of a large heat tunnel, fitted with conveyors, water sprays, pumps and heaters. It also uses expensive energy, although modern tunnels make use of heat exchangers between the various stages of heating and cooling.

Accurate temperature control is paramount if the quality of the wine is to be protected. Criticisms similar to those of thermotic bottling could be levelled at tunnel pasteurisation if it is carelessly operated. Yet this technique is widely used, even for sparkling wines, where one might expect the internal pressure to shatter the glass.

Flash pasteurisation

Pasteurised milk is treated by flash pasteurisation, which has been standard practice for years as a protection against the many harmful organisms that milk can carry. It was a simple step to adapt this method for the packing of wine. Wine is intrinsically a much lower risk substance than milk, so it is not necessary to use such stringent conditions.

A flash pasteuriser is a heat exchanger that is capable of raising the temperature of a liquid rapidly to a high temperature, and then as rapidly bringing it down again, literally 'in a flash'. The temperature reached is 95°C, but it is held there for only one to two seconds before it is cooled down again, to prevent any hint of cooking.

14.3 A heat exchanger

The equipment for this type of bottling is simple, consisting of a metal plate heat exchanger placed between the wine vat and the bottling machine. The wine is heated and cooled before reaching the filler, which effectively knocks out all the yeasts and bacteria. However, this simplicity conceals a potential problem, the wine being sterilised before being bottled. It is easily re-infected by the bottling machinery and the bottling materials, in fact by anything with which it comes into contact.

This necessitates the operation of the process by people who have been trained in sterile techniques, people who understand that yeasts are in the air around us, on all surfaces, on our hands. The filling machinery and pipework must be sterilised before use, with the aid of sterilising chemicals such as hydrogen peroxide, or hypochlorites as in common bleach.

An alternative way of sterilising bottling machinery is by the use of heat, the critical parameters being that the external surfaces must reach 82°C and remain at that temperature for at least 20 minutes. The most effective method is flushing with hot water at 90°C, which cleans and sterilise at the same time. Steam is sometimes used for this purpose, but whilst being an effective sterilant, it does not possess the cleansing property of a current of hot water. Any traces of wine that remain from the previous bottling (that should have been removed by rinsing) become baked on and form a solid deposit that can subsequently re-appear as 'floaters' in the next wine.

Bottles should be freshly purchased from the glassworks, and must be received packed in good pallets, tightly shrink-wrapped. They should not be stored for longer than a month, in case they become contaminated. Corks must be purchased in sealed plastic bags, sterilised either by sulphur dioxide or gamma radiation.

All of these conditions are relatively easy to manage, provided everyone involved is given adequate training. Flash pasteurisation and cold sterile filtration have become widely used techniques in the wine trade.

Cold sterile filtration

If heating is to be avoided, the only alternative process for bottling is to use filtration techniques to remove the micro-organisms, a technique known as cold sterile filtration.

Filtration for aseptic bottling has become probably the most widely used technique of all because it is simple to operate, cheap and reliable. It does have its antagonists, who claim that filtration removes the heart and soul of the wine and should never be used. In reality, it depends on the way in which it is used: if used intelligently and sensibly, the effect on the wine is imperceptible. Comparative tastings have sometimes taken place immediately after filtration, when a difference has been detected. The only fair test for the effect of filtration is to allow the wines to rest a few weeks in bottle before tasting.

When a wine has reached the bottling stage, it should have received its initial filtration through kieselguhr and should already be clear and bright. It might still, however, contain low levels or yeast and bacteria, which will be removed by the next filtration, which should be sheets of a tight formulation. This is the stage where the greatest damage can be done, by the over-zealous use of filter sheets that are of too dense a structure and can actually strip the wine of body and flavour. Sheets are available in a wide range of grades, which enables the choice of the correct structure to be made, relative to the wine to be filtered.

Before the days of the ubiquitous membrane filter, sheet filtration was regarded as the final treatment, being perfectly capable of removing all the yeasts and the bacteria, provided it is correctly operated. It is the latter caveat that has seen the tremendous rise in the use of membranes, for they offer the security and peace of mind that all bottling operators seek, so that they can sleep at night in the confidence that the highly susceptible wine that they have just bottled will remain stable until opened for consumption.

The final membrane, which should always be situated as close to the filling machine as possible, takes out any stray yeasts that might have got through the sheet filter or that might have survived the sterilisation process in the machinery. Membranes are extremely tough, are easily sterilised, and will hold back anything larger than the size of the pores, but care is still needed, as dirt will easily block them and replacements are expensive.

The crucial parameter at this stage is the choice of pore size. The zealous technologist must be curbed by the winemaker and encouraged to use only the pore size that is necessary for the removal of troublesome micro-organisms. For a big and fat red wine it might be possible to dispense with the membrane altogether. A lighter red wine might need a 1.2µ to remove only the yeasts, whereas a rosé or a white could tolerate a 0.65µ or even a 0.45µ to no detriment. Using a 0.45µ membrane for all wines makes life simple, but does pose a risk to the quality of heavier red wines.

The critical control points for success are the following:

1. Ensuring that all bottles and closures are purchased in a sterile condition.

2. Training the operators in aseptic techniques: an awareness that we are surrounded by micro-organisms that must not be allowed to contaminate the bottled wine.

3. Sterilising the filling machinery and testing for the absence of yeasts and bacteria.

4. Filtering the wine carefully through kieselguhr, then sheets, and finally a membrane of an appropriate pore size.

5. Filling the bottles and corking them quickly.

After filling, samples should always be tested for the absence of yeasts and bacteria before releasing for sale. Even the most well organised operation has occasional failures, but a product re-call is very expensive. The cost of re-bottling is much less if the product is still in the warehouse.

Chapter 15

WINE FAULTS

Wine kept for two or three years develops great poison.

Chinese 14th century

Old books on the technical aspects of wine list a range of troubles that are virtually never encountered nowadays, many of which were of microbiological origin and have been eliminated by improvements in filtration and aseptic techniques. Better control of antioxidants has reduced the number of oxidised bottles on the shelf, and the improved quality of packaging materials has almost eliminated foreign body complaints.

The following problems remain and will be difficult to eliminate totally, and consumers should not be afraid to take bottles back to the retailer. Although all retailers are very willing to refund the money or replace the bottle, some even giving a free bottle as well, most take little interest in recording the proper details of the fault, simply registering the returned bottle as 'Quality complaint'. This is most unhelpful, as the producer of the wine has no facts on which to base any investigation, with no chance of continuous improvement, or of reducing the incidence of faulty bottles. It has also resulted in the cork being wrongly blamed, when the cork has been entirely innocent. This situation has come about because many people, including highly qualified members of the wine trade, have no idea how to recognise faults in wine.

Beyond shelf-life

Contrary to the belief of many consumers, wine does not have an infinite life in bottle; neither do all wines improve with keeping. In fact, more and more wines are made for immediate consumption and actually deteriorate with time. A glance at the back label of wines on a supermarket shelf will soon confirm this, with the frequent recommendation that 'This wine should be consumed within six months of purchase'. This is the popular modern style of wine for which many consumers are searching. But this wine has insufficient structure for long life. Wines that improve with keeping must have more concentration, more body, and especially higher levels of the polyphenols, the natural preservatives.

It is important to differentiate between natural decomposition and oxidation. Wines that have reached the end of their natural life are not necessarily oxidised. The fruit components simply break down, leaving the wine dull and lacking in any character, and this can happen in the absence of oxygen.

Although shelf life is primarily dependent on the style and structure of the original wine, the ingress of oxygen hastens the deterioration. For a given wine, the shelf life is influenced by the material of the packaging, which affects the rate of oxidation. Those materials with the greatest oxygen barrier, such as glass bottles and metal caps, will confer on the wine the maximum shelf life. Packages such as plastic bottles and bag-in-boxes which, despite the best efforts of technologists, do not provide a total barrier to oxygen, result in a reduced shelf life. Stock control of these items is of paramount importance if stale wine is to be avoided.

The 'surface effect' (see p.163) also influences the shelf life of wines in all forms of package. The longest shelf life occurs in a large bottle made of glass, such as a magnum (1.5 litres), or, even better, in a nebuchadnezzar, which holds 16 litres. The worst conditions are to be found in a small bottle, such as the standard airline size of 18.75cl, especially if it is made of PET. Such bottles are in use, and are ideal for certain circumstances such as in-flight service, but the short life of only some three to six months has to be taken into account when planning for stock holding.

It might seem strange that there is no provision for a "Best before" date on wine labels. There is a general requirement in Europe that all foodstuff with a shelf life of less than 72 weeks should carry such an indication. However, wine is exempt from this legislation, presumably on the assumption that all wine has a shelf life exceeding 72 weeks. This, of course, is incorrect in the case of small PET bottles and bag-in-box. However, this anomaly remains, and a "Best before" date is not allowed. The best that can be done legally is a recommendation for usage before a set period after purchase, as above.

Oxidation

Oxidation can occur in any wine, and should be distinguished from a wine that is simply beyond its shelf life. Oxidation occurs in wines when they lose the protection of anti-oxidants, both natural and added, and oxygen from the atmosphere attacks the wine, assisting the breakdown of the fruit components.

The first indication of an oxidised wine is a loss of its attractive colour:

- White wines that should be a clear lemon yellow with green tints become a dull brown straw.

- Rosé wines that started life as vibrant pinks become a pale orange-pink, or even a brown pink. (Caution is needed here, as some rosé wines are an orange-pink when first produced.)

- Red wines lose the deep purple red or ruby colour and become paler, with an orange or brown rim.

The bouquet of the wine becomes tired, losing its freshness and smelling of caramel or even 'meaty' (like beef extract). The palate confirms the impressions of the nose.

When a wine is packed it should have been brought into the correct condition by first carrying out a complete analysis, followed by any necessary treatments or additions, especially the adjustment of the free sulphur dioxide level. However, if the wine has been allowed to absorb quantities of oxygen from the atmosphere because of careless handling or storage, the sulphur dioxide in the wine will quickly be destroyed after packing, leaving the wine prone to early deterioration.

Tartrate crystals

Tartrate crystals in a bottle are regarded as a fault by most consumers, despite any arguments to the contrary. This deposit is not tartaric acid, as is commonly thought, but is either calcium tartrate or potassium bi-tartrate (cream of tartar), originating in the grape. This is caused either by a poorly conducted stabilisation process, or by the presence of protective colloids which have prevented the deposition of the crystals during the stabilisation process and which have subsequently denatured. Of course, they may be intentional, in that the winemaker preferred to bottle the wine untreated.

Two understandable fears that are generated in the minds of consumers are that the wine contains broken glass or added sugar, although this latter observation is irrational because sugar would not remain un-dissolved.

15.1 Tartrate crystals

Tartrate crystals in a bottle of wine are probably the biggest cause of complaint in the wine trade. The best that can be done to prevent this phenomenon is to fine the wine thoroughly, testing for the complete removal of colloids, and then to submit it to treatment by the contact process, testing for tartrate stability by one of the modern methods. Unfortunately, despite the best efforts of winemakers and bottlers, crystals sometimes still come down. Perhaps an explanatory back label would make the crystals acceptable, especially if imaginatively worded, as in one old German label that read "This wine contains Wine Diamonds, which are an entirely natural deposit"!

A great deal of expense, energy and effort have gone into the prevention of these deposits, adding a significant amount to the cost of the wine, with also a possible loss of quality. All that is necessary is to decant the wine slowly, when the crystals will remain in the bottle. If they get into the glass, they will probably remain there, stuck by surface tension and even if they get into the mouth, they are completely harmless, merely tasting slightly bitter. After all, they are only cream of tartar, as used in baking. If only the consumer could be educated to understand what tartrate crystals are and why they are there, life would be so much simpler for the winemaker.

The only way of dealing with stocks of wine which are showing crystal deposits is to open the bottles, tip the wine back into a vat, submit the wine to refrigeration and re-bottle. It is quite possible that the refrigeration treatment is unnecessary, all the crystals having deposited in the original bottles, but it is safer to err on the side of caution.

Cork taint

Wine tainted by a cork is commonly called 'corked' or 'corky'. This is an unmistakable musty smell resembling fungi or autumnal woodlands, and renders the wine undrinkable, although still harmless. Such bottles should be sent back or returned to the retailer. Care should be taken before making a final judgement, however, because a somewhat similar earthy note is a natural characteristic of some grape varieties. Furthermore, the untrained nose finds it difficult to distinguish between cork taint, oxidation and other out-of-condition wines, frequently blaming the cork, when it is entirely innocent.

It should be particularly noted that wine containing small pieces of cork as a result of a brittle cork breaking up is *not* corky. It is not even faulty. The remedy here is simple: fish the pieces out with a finger or a spoon and carry on drinking!

Volatile acidity

Wine with excess volatile acidity is the result of careless wine handling techniques, with bacteria running rampant, a shortage of free sulphur dioxide and an ample supply of dissolved oxygen, all of which are avoidable situations. The bacteria convert alcohol to acetic acid (the acid of vinegar), which then reacts with further alcohol to produce the ester known as ethyl acetate. The wine becomes undrinkable, smelling of nail varnish or cellulose paint (both of which are based upon ethyl acetate) and tasting of vinegar (acetic acid).

The only use for such a bottle is to consign it to the vinegar pot and encourage it by aeration to continue its evolution to wine vinegar.

For further information on volatile acidity, see p.89.

Second fermentation

Wines made by fermentation to dryness, and containing no fermentable sugars, are stable towards further fermentation and can safely be bottled by traditional methods without the risk of a second fermentation occurring. However, this is not the case with many modern wines that contain any fermentable sugars, however small in quantity. These wines are susceptible to re-fermentation by stray yeasts and must be bottled aseptically.

When a yeast starts a fermentation in the bottle the effects are obvious: the wine goes cloudy and the cork starts to rise due to the pressure of the carbon dioxide that is being produced. Bag-in-box packages can be even more dramatic, blowing up like footballs and eventually bursting, with the resultant chaos of collapsing pallets and aromatic warehouses!

The only treatment for wines that are undergoing a second fermentation is to disgorge them and filter them quickly to remove the yeast. After analysis and correction of the sulphur dioxide content they can be re-bottled, provided the style of the wine has not been altered. The procedures in the bottling plant should then be closely examined to determine the cause of the problem, and corrective action implemented.

A critical tasting and analysis of the sugar content will be necessary to ensure that the style has not been affected adversely. Adjustment of the sulphur dioxide level is particularly important in these circumstances, because the yeast activity destroys all the existing sulphur dioxide.

The incidence of second fermentation has diminished greatly in recent years. With improved equipment and better knowledge this fault should be extremely rare. Its presence indicates bad hygiene or ignored procedures.

Iron casse

Excess iron dissolved in wine can result in a white precipitate or deposit in the bottle formed by a reaction between iron and the phosphates in the wine. This is traditionally known as iron casse, from the French word 'casse', which has the same meaning as the English word 'precipitate', something which has been thrown out of solution. The prevention of this fault is either by blue fining to reduce the iron level, or by the addition of citric acid, which prevents the formation of the precipitate.

The precipitate is harmless, as is the wine, which can be decanted off the solid matter and drunk normally.

Copper casse

Copper casse is easily recognisable as a brown haze in the wine, with the mysterious property of disappearing when the bottle is opened. This is because copper casse is a complex of cuprous ions and proteins, which can only form in anaerobic conditions, such as are found inside an unopened bottle. When the bottle is opened and the wine becomes aerated, the cuprous ions are oxidised to cupric ions, which breaks the complex and the haze disappears.

Wine with copper casse should be regarded with more caution than wine with iron casse because copper is toxic at high concentrations, although it is an essential trace element in the diet.

Mousiness

Sometimes, but rarely in these days of improved bottling techniques, a wine can develop a smell of mouse droppings, often more apparent on the aftertaste than on the nose. This is due to an infection of either a lactic acid bacterium or a particular yeast of the *Brettanomyces* genus. Both of these organisms are easily controlled by sulphur dioxide and can be removed from the wine by membrane filtration prior to bottling. A mousy smell is a sign of poor hygiene, and once it has affected the wine, there is little that can be done in the way of rescue.

Geranium smell

Another result of bacterial contamination can be the development of a powerful smell of geraniums (pelargoniums, to be precise). This is caused when a certain strain of lactic acid bacteria infects a wine containing sorbic acid which the bacteria metabolise, producing a substance known as 2-ethoxyhexa-3:5-diene. As with mousiness, wines which have developed this fault are fit only for destruction. Likewise, the root cause is poor winery hygiene, but this problem is avoidable simply by not using sorbic acid as an additive.

Chapter 16

LEGISLATION & REGULATIONS

La liberte est le droit de faire tout ce que les lois permettent
(Freedom is the right to do anything the laws permit)

Montesquieu, 1689-1755

Wine is more tightly regulated in the European Union (EU) than any other food product. This should be very heartening for consumers, who can rest assured that the wine they are drinking has been produced and bottled under a very strict régime. The integration of UK traditions into a European standard has not always been an easy passage, as witness the attempts to prohibit the use of old British terms such as 'claret' for the red wines of Bordeaux (after the French word Clairet, meaning a light red wine), or the word 'hock' for wines from the Rhine, named after the village of Hochheim and made famous as the favourite wines of Queen Victoria.

These differences have now been resolved and the result is a very complex corpus of wine regulations. There can be no doubt that the information on a wine label is much more specific than that on the labels of other foodstuffs, which can still be misleading and yet be within the law. For producers and bottlers, some of the regulations are tedious, and others appear irrelevant, but most are welcomed and contribute significantly to the control of a widely produced and easily counterfeited beverage. There are some, however, who would claim that the European wine industry is over regulated, putting it at a disadvantage when compared with third countries.

There is a vast raft of legislation relating to foodstuffs, and anyone involved in the production and sale of wine should be aware of its existence.

Although EU Regulations automatically become law in the UK, The Common Agricultural Policy (Wine) Regulations form the Statutory Instrument by which the legislation is enforced. In the wholesale sector the enforcement authorities are the Ministry of Agriculture, Fisheries and Food, HM Customs and Excise and the Wine Standards Board. Enforcement in the retail sector is uniquely by Local Authorities.

The following regulations, and their many subsequent amendments, are particularly pertinent to wine:

1493/1999 The Common Organisation of the Market in Wine

This is the latest version of the principal regulation controlling the *production* of wine (despite its possibly misleading title), and contains many of the basic controls of wine production, and is an essential document for anybody who is interested in the mechanics of wine production.

The Regulation is not easy to comprehend, the sequence being not entirely logical and the scope rather wide, ranging from the planting and grubbing-up of vines to market mechanisms. However, the eight annexes are very useful, ranging from product definitions, alcoholic strengths, wine-growing zones, authorised oenological practices, quality wines regulations, to basic labelling requirements.

2392/89 General Rules for Description and Presentation

This, the second most important regulation, deals with general *labelling* matters. Chapter 1 defines the requirements for products originating within the Community and includes table wines and quality wines produced in specified regions, and Chapter 2 deals with products originating in third countries.

One of the principles introduced by these regulations is that there are two main categories of information that can appear on the label: the mandatory information and a list of optional information. All Community legislation is what is known as 'positive legislation' – if the regulations do not specifically say that something can be done, then it cannot. Thus, anything that is not specified within these lists is forbidden. This has caused much controversy, because, for example, there is no provision for a 'best before' date. Neither is there provision for units of alcohol.

A wonderful example of the chauvinism of the EU is enshrined in the definitions of the basic categories: Community wine can be classified as table wine or quality wine; wine from a third country can only be called wine.

The mandatory information for the lowest level of wine is:

- The words "table wine" for EU wines, or "wine" for third country wines
- Country of origin
- Name and head office address of the responsible packer
- For third country wines, the name and address of the importer
- Nominal volume
- Actual alcoholic strength, expressed as % vol

It is interesting to note that it is never mandatory for the name of the producer to appear on the label, but only the bottler.

The optional information includes:

- Description of colour and style
- Brand name
- Name and address of retailer and distributor
- Use recommendation (e.g. 'Serve chilled')
- The e-mark (see below)

The use recommendation is sometimes cleverly extended to include an indication of shelf life by the use of a phrase such as "Best consumed within six months of purchase". It should be noted that a "Best before" date, *per se*, is not permitted.

There are incredibly detailed rules regarding minimum heights and relative sizes of lettering:

- The name and address of the packer must not be more than half the height of the characters used for the words "table wine"

- Nominal volume and alcoholic strength must be not less than 3mm in height for a 75cl bottle
- The e-mark must be not less than 3mm in height for all bottle sizes.

Quality wines must give the quality status and the specified region, and any wine that has no specific regional origin cannot state a grape variety. If a label states one grape variety, then the wine must contain at least 85% of that variety. If the label mentions two varieties, then the wine must be made entirely from them.

3201/90 Detailed Rules for Description and Presentation

The annexes to this regulation are probably more important than the regulation itself, covering the following important topics:

- List of terms denoting superior quality for third country wines
- Geographical areas for third countries
- Synonyms for vine varieties
- Vine varieties for third country wines

2333/92 Description and Presentation of Sparkling Wines

The labelling regulations for sparkling wines are similar to those for light wines.

1601/91 Description and Presentation of Aromatised Wines

These regulations cover vermouth and any other wine to which flavouring has been added (but not gin, which is governed by spirits regulations).

Weights & Measures (Packaged Goods) Regulations 1979

All pre-packaged foodstuffs are now packed according to the European average system of quantity, which is different from the old British system of minimum quantity. Under the British system, every bottle of wine had to contain at least the quantity stated on the label (the nominal quantity). With the average system, the entire batch of wine is regarded as the unit, i.e. the average of all the bottles in the batch must be not less than the nominal quantity, but each individual bottle can be above or below the nominal, within certain limits.

The lower limit is governed by the tolerable negative error (TNE) which for a 750 ml bottle is 15ml. Up to $2^1/_2\%$ of the batch can have negative errors greater than this, but no bottle is allowed an error greater than twice the TNE, which is 30ml. Therefore, a 750 ml bottle of wine is allowed to fall as low as 720ml, but because the average for the batch must be at least 750ml, some lucky people will get more. In practice, wine filling is much more even than this and most bottles will hold between 740ml and 760ml.

When this average system is certified as having been used by a packer, and it has been checked by the local authority for weights and measures, the e-mark may be put on the label. If the wine has been bottled within the EU, the shipper of such wine need not be concerned with any further checking. The responsibility for correct filling lies with the authority in whose area the wine was packed. For wines from third countries, the importer should satisfy himself that proper testing has taken place, with suitable documentary evidence.

Food (Lot Marking) Regulations 1992

Under this regulation all foodstuffs must carry a lot mark to enable a product re-call to be carried out quickly and efficiently, if necessary. This must commence with a capital L and must be a number unique to a batch. The size of a batch is not defined; it must merely be identifiable. It might be a day's bottling, but equally it might be the entire vintage. It is advantageous, however, to keep the batch as small as possible, in case of any re-calls.

Most bottlers of wine use a format of four digits, where the first digit is the last digit of the year, and the other three are the day of the year, according to the Julian calendar. For example, January 31st of 1999 would be L9031.

Food Labelling Regulations 1996

These regulations consolidate and replace the Food Labelling Regulations 1984 and include, for the first time, a requirement for the quantitative declaration of ingredients, where the labelling of the food places special emphasis on the presence or low content of an ingredient. It should be noted that wine, *inter alia*, is exempt from these regulations by virtue of the fact that it is both a single ingredient foodstuff and is tightly regulated by its own régime (see above).

Not only is wine exempt from ingredient listing, but it is actually illegal to print a list of ingredients on a wine label, as ingredients are not among the optional items that can be quoted if desired. Opposition to this amongst the wine trade is not due to any shame that producers might have in the way they make their wine: a full list of all the permitted oenological practices is easily available (see above, Regulation 1493/1999). Problems arise in trying to keep track of all the (permitted) additives and treatments in a large-scale blend of many different components. Similarly, it is sometimes difficult to determine whether an additive is an ingredient or a treatment, and whether any of the additive remains in the finished wine.

It should not be forgotten that European legislation is positive legislation, in that if something is not specifically permitted, then it is forbidden. This is the opposite to earlier UK legislation, in which everything was permitted, unless specifically forbidden. Another transgression of the law by some of the major retailers has been the inclusion of items such as 'units of alcohol' on their back labels. The EU disapproves of the concept of units of alcohol because it is a dangerous way of calculating the safe amount of wine to consume; each one of us reacts differently to alcohol.

The labelling regulations relating to wine, as they stand at present, are actually very much more stringent and more informative than those applying to other foodstuffs, where it is often impossible to determine the true origin or packer. A wine label will always give, at least, the name and address of the bottler – even though a little code-breaking might be necessary!

Food Safety Act 1990

The Food Act 1984 was virtually repealed by the Food Safety Act 1990, which changed the whole face of the UK food industry and introduced a new approach to quality. It swept away the old system of warranties whereby a supplier was able to hide behind a piece of paper that stated that the product he had sold was perfect. In its place was introduced the concept of 'due diligence', whereby it behoves the supplier to take positive action to ensure that his goods are up to the standard expected, rather than relying on a somewhat valueless piece of paper.

The aspects of food safety introduced by the Act include the registration and inspection of premises, the issue of compulsory improvement notices, training, temperature control, a food hazard warning system and many more.

The Food Safety Act has become synonymous with the phrase 'due diligence', which in some ways is unfortunate. Firstly, this phrase is but one small part of an Act which introduced wide-ranging changes to food law, and secondly because it is associated with a defence against prosecution rather than positive action. The 'due diligence' phrase appears in chapter 16 section 21(1) where it states that it shall "be a defence for the person charged to prove that he took all reasonable precautions and exercised all due diligence to avoid the commission of the offence". The result of this is that the large retailers have taken extreme measures to ensure that their wine suppliers are satisfactory by insisting on quality audits carried out by their own technologists. This is good for the audit industry, but irritating to the suppliers who have to endure multiple audits by each individual customer.

Food Safety (General Food Hygiene) Regulations 1995

Spawned by the Food Safety Act 1990, these Regulations lay down the detailed requirements for hygiene standards within all stages of the food chain.

One of the most interesting concepts introduced is Hazard Analysis and Critical Control Point (HACCP) System which is dealt with in chapter 17. This procedure has been incorporated in European hygiene legislation and should, therefore, be addressed in all EU member states.

Materials and Articles in Contact with Food Regulations 1987

These require that materials and articles intended to come into contact with food shall be manufactured in such a way that they do not transfer their constituents to food in quantities which could endanger health or cause a deterioration in the food.

Plastic Materials and Articles in Contact with Food Regulations 1992

These regulations limit the transfer of monomers from plastic materials to 60 mg per kilogram of food. All plastic packaging materials for wine, such as PET bottles, bag-in-box bags and plastic stoppers must conform to this legislation.

Environmental Protection Act 1990

This Act controls the way in which businesses must prevent pollution of the environment, including air, water, the disposal of waste, litter, noise and the use, storage and transport of hazardous substances.

Producer Responsibility Obligations (Packaging Waste) Regulations

These lay down the objectives set by EC Directive 94/62, with targets to be achieved by 2001:

- To recover 50% by weight of the national packaging waste

- To recycle 15% by weight of each packaging material.

The proportions of the responsibilities have been allocated to the various parts of the supply chain:

- The raw material manufacturer: 6%

- The converter (the one who makes the package): 11%

- The packer or filler: 36%

- The retailer: 47%

Small businesses that handle less than 50 tonnes of packaging per annum (equivalent to 8500 cases of 12) are exempt from this responsibility.

For further reading:
In the UK all legislation is obtainable from HM Stationery Office or their nominated bookshops

Chapter 17

QUALITY ASSURANCE

All men who live with any degree of serenity live by some assurance of grace.

Rheinhold Niebuhr, 1892-1971

All the art and science of winemaking is wasted if there is no system for assuring the preservation of the potential that is being realised during the production of the wine.

First, it is important to differentiate between quality control and quality assurance. Quality assurance is a general concept, covering the manner in which a business is organised, so that the quality of its product is assured at all stages. As applied to a wine business, good quality assurance will ensure that the original potential of the wine is not lost on the way to the bottle. Quality assurance is the totality of all the management actions and procedures that set out to achieve this high standard, and this will incorporate quality control.

Quality control is a 'hands on' process of monitoring and controlling all parameters that effect the quality of the product at all stages of production, from the planting of the vineyard to the storing of the bottled wine. Quality control is not just something that technicians perform in a laboratory, but should be a sequence of observations that are applied by everyone who has any part to play throughout the process. It is worrying to go into a production establishment and see a door marked 'Quality Control Department' – such a thing should not exist, because the responsibility for quality rests with everyone involved in production.

There are several models on which to base a quality assurance programme, models that help by providing a standard base from which to work. In the food industry the most important of these is Hazard Analysis, not least because it is required by law. This is the best base from which to start. Having developed this, the next step might well be to aim for registration to ISO 9000, a quality management system which ISO 9000 has proved to be within reach of any well-organised company, however small. Following on from these, there are many further steps to improvements in quality management, such as Total Quality Management (TQM), which introduces the concept of a business being a succession of processes, where everyone is both supplier and customer in a chain of events. In this case, customer satisfaction is required throughout the business, and not just from the ultimate external customer. Or there is the Japanese concept of Kaizen, where continuous improvement in small steps is demanded.

There are many ways in which the profile of quality can be raised. The important factor is that it should not be disregarded, but should always be an integral part of any business plan, being equally important to profit or expansion.

Hazard analysis (HACCP)

Hazard Analysis and Critical Control Point (HACCP) System is a system of food control developed in the 1960's jointly by the Pillsbury Company, the US Army Laboratories and NASA, to ensure the safety of foods for the American space programme. It is essentially an exercise in preventative action and, although originally aimed at preventing microbiological contamination, it can be used for any aspect of manufacture and can deal with any hazard, whether physical, chemical or microbiological. It can also be made as broad or as detailed as desired. The danger is in becoming too detailed, when the process becomes very long-winded and tedious. The important criterion is getting the guidelines correct in the first instance, which requires experience.

The sudden popularity of hazard analysis in the UK is due to the fact that it has been specified as an actual requirement in The Food Safety (General Food Hygiene) Regulations 1995, which were enacted to satisfy the requirements of The Food Hygiene Directive 93/43/EEC of 14 June 1993. Section 4.(3) states "The proprietor of a food business shall identify any step in the activities of the food business which is critical to ensuring food safety . . ."

The process commences in an entirely theoretical manner, with a group of experts round a table, each contributing from their own experience to the creation a list of every possible hazard that could affect the production of the food. The hazards are then analysed critically to determine whether they pose a threat to quality. Those that are critical are the Critical Control Points (CCP), which are defined as: "A step at which control can be applied and is essential to prevent or eliminate a food safety *(or quality)* hazard or reduce it to an acceptable level."

Having completed the theoretical process, it is transferred to practice and becomes an active part of quality assurance procedures.

The process is carried out in steps:

1. The guidelines are laid down defining precisely the area to be investigated and the ultimate objective. It may well be too difficult to take the business as a whole, so it should be broken down into manageable parts, which for a winery might be:

    The handling of grapes – the fermentation process – the storage of wine in bulk – the management of dry goods – the bottling process.

2. A multi-disciplinary team of experts is formed, covering all aspects of the part of the process chosen. For a bottling operation, this might include an oenologist, a winery manager, an experienced quality control technologist, a bottling supervisor, a dry goods buyer and an engineer. It is important that there should be an input from all aspects of the operation.

3. A process flow chart is constructed, breaking the process down into individual steps, showing every discrete sequential part of the operation. The purpose of this is to ensure that every step in the process has been considered and to help to concentrate the mind on each step. After construction of the chart, it is good practice to walk through the steps at the actual site, confirming

that the chart is accurate.

4. Each step is considered and the hazards at that step identified and listed.

5. Each hazard is examined for the degree of risk and for the control measures that can be applied to prevent the fault occurring.

6. By the use of a 'decision tree' or other logical process, each hazard is examined to decide whether it lies at a critical control point.

7. A documented monitoring system is established, setting target levels and tolerances where possible, frequency of monitoring and the personnel responsible.

8. A preventative action plan is set up to establish that each CCP is in control and that appropriate action is taken if it goes out of control.

9. The plan is reviewed on a regular basis, with the object of gradually removing CCPs by putting in place effective control measures.

Earlier forms of HACCP included a numerical estimate of the degree of seriousness of each risk, using a logarithmic sequence of negative points, such as:

1000 points	Serious risk to the business
100 points	Serious risk to the product, but not the business
10 points	Some risk to the product, but not a major non-conformance
1 point	A risk easily overcome, and no lasting effect

This idea has been dropped in later versions of HACCP, possibly because too much time and effort went into a decision on the value of each risk. However, if it can be managed, the use of numerical values gives a means of monitoring progress, because each subsequent review should show a progressive reduction in negative points, as each CCP is eliminated.

ISO 9000

ISO 9000 is one of many quality management systems that assist a business to manage the quality of its product or service in a systematic manner. It is based on the total documentation of the business procedures, a tight internal control of the system and an on-going assessment by an accredited body.

It began life after the Second World War (1939-1945) in munitions factories, where armaments were exploding prematurely, with somewhat dire results. It was realised that formal procedures were required to ensure consistency of production, which led to the development by NATO of the Allied Quality Assurance Publications (AQAP) series of standards. These were developed into standards for the wider field of engineering, and in 1979 were published by the British Standards Institution as BS 5750. The success of this British standard became world-wide and it was adopted by the International Standards Organisation as ISO 9000.

There are three variants of the Standard, each applicable to a different type of industry:

- ISO 9001 : Manufacturing or service industry that includes design
- ISO 9002 : Design requirements are not included
- ISO 9003 : Businesses concerned only with final inspection and tests

The Mobil Survey 1996 showed the following distribution of certificates world-wide: ISO 9001 : 33%   ISO 9002 : 66% ISO 9003 : 1%

The criticisms of ISO 9000

The greatest criticism of ISO 9000 is that it does not guarantee the quality of the product. What is does guarantee is consistency, because everything has to be done in a uniform fashion, time and time again, with the same result, day in, day out. The quality level might be high or might be low, but it will be the same.

Some would say that ISO 9000 is bureaucratic and causes a vast increase in paperwork, general workload and costs. This could and does happen, but it is entirely dependent upon the manner in which the system is installed: done properly, the result is the exact opposite.

Probably the major criticism of ISO 9000 is that the control of work processes by documented procedures results in stagnation. As one critic has put it: "<u>Control</u> of output does not <u>improve</u> output." This could be the case, but would not happen in a well-constructed system, because the concept of continuous improvement would be built in. The infra-structure is already there – nonconformance procedures, preventative action procedures, internal auditing. All of these can be made to incorporate continuous improvement, provided the right attitude is engendered at the start.

The benefits of ISO 9000

Preparations for installation of the systems required by ISO 9000 give an excellent opportunity to examine, review and improve existing systems. In the course of this, people are involved and motivated, which automatically improves communication.

The result, when all the procedures are in place, is that a new-found clarity emerges, where everyone knows who does what, how they do it and whose responsibility it is.

Both internally and externally, a commitment to quality is demonstrated, which raises morale and impresses customers. Costs are reduced, both by increased efficiency and by reduced wastage, because the structures that are put in place are aimed at getting it right first time. In a survey by Irwin, Dunn & Bradstreet in 1996, 85% or respondents claimed they had experienced external benefits since registration and 95% had experienced internal benefits.

ISO 9000 was designed to help a business: if it is proving a hindrance, it has been wrongly installed.

The Twenty Requirements

1. *Management responsibility*   The total commitment of management is demanded, with a meaningful quality policy, stating the objectives for quality and the commitment to them, in relation to organisational goals and the expectations of its customers. This policy must be understood, implemented and maintained at all levels within the company. There must be adequate resources, including the appointment of a management representative to manage the system, and a review at management level on a regular basis.

2. *The quality system* All procedures must be documented (written down) and maintained in current status. One might well ask the question: why should everything be committed to paper, because this is tedious, time-consuming and unnecessary? The answer is simply that it makes good common sense to document what is done, as there will be fewer mistakes and a greater chance of doing it right first time, and everybody will do it in the same way.

3. *Contract review* A most important section, requiring structured dialogue with every customer, to ensure that they receive precisely what they expect.

4. *Design control*   An extension of contract review, where the designing of a new product is involved.

5. *Document and data control*   Documents and data must be properly controlled, kept up-to-date and correctly distributed.

6. *Purchasing* All suppliers and subcontractors must be approved before use by a systematic screening process.

7. *Control of customer-supplied items* Anything supplied by the customer for incorporation in the final product, the so-called 'free-issue' items, must be given the same care and attention as the company's own items. An example of this would be electrical alternators made by specialist manufacturers which are incorporated into cars.

8. *Product identification and traceability* "Where appropriate . ."

product should be identifiable throughout the process. For all food products, this is mandatory, by European law.

9. *Process control* In manufacturing, this section occupies most of the manuals, as this covers the entire process of production. Procedures and work instructions are required for all aspects of the manufacture of the product.

10. *Inspection and testing* Procedures are required for all stages of testing: incoming materials, in-process checks, finished product tests and the production of records and results that prove that the tests have been done.

11. *Control of inspection, measuring and test equipment* It is not sufficient merely to test the product, but the test equipment must be tested to a pre-defined programme, to ensure that it is giving accurate results.

12. *Inspection and test status* It must be made obvious whether goods have not been tested, have been tested and are awaiting results, or have been cleared for delivery.

13. *Control of nonconforming product* Goods that are imperfect in some way must be readily identifiable and must be prevented from the possibility of delivery. Their disposal must be agreed.

14. *Corrective and preventive action* Probably the most positive and helpful requirement, leading to continuous improvement, if handled well. It covers the action necessary to correct a fault and prevent it happening again. This is corrective action, but better still is preventive action, which forestalls problems and prevents them ever happening.

15. *Handling, storage, packaging, preservation and delivery* All the moments when good quality could be destroyed! Procedures are required that prevent damage after production.

16. *Control of quality records* Records form a useful history of production. If they are lost or damaged, important information is lost for ever.

17. *Internal quality audits* Internal checking by departments of one

another keeps the system alive, provided it is done in the right way and is not seen as 'snooping' or 'prying'. Without internal auditing, the quality system becomes fossilised.

Earlier attempts at documenting procedures failed because there was no way of checking that they were accurate or, indeed, even in use. With ISO 9000 this cannot happen, because all procedures have to be audited regularly and reviewed by management; training requirements have to be documented; mistakes cannot be hidden.

18. *Training* All expertise comes of training. This section requires that all employees, at whatever level, be given the training needed for them to do a good job.

19. *Servicing* This requirement applies only to those companies that have an obligation for after-sales service.

20. *Statistical techniques* The standard is merely trying to persuade companies to investigate the usefulness of statistical techniques for the analysis of its activities. There is no obligation to use statistical techniques.

Before granting registration, the certification body, which should itself be accredited by the national accreditation body (which in the UK is UKAS – the United Kingdom Accreditation Service), carries out a detailed assessment of the entire system. Return visits are made periodically for a long as the registration remains valid.

In summary, ISO 9000 is common sense written down on paper. It is a system that enforces a discipline. Handled correctly, it does not stifle development or prevent change. It is meant to be an aid to the achievement of quality: if it is not, then it has been badly installed and should be re-visited. It is due for revision in 2000,when many of its present criticisms will be addressed. Two major changes will be the incorporation of a guarantee of the quality of the product or service, and the introduction of the concept of continuous improvement.

For further reading:

- **For HACCP**: Codex Alimentarius Food Hygiene Basic Texts.

Food and Agriculture Organisation of the United Nations/World Health Organisation, ISBN 92-5-104021-4

- **For ISO 9000**: ISO 9001 : 1994

International Organisation for Standardisation (ISO) or from British Standards Institution (BSI), ISBN 0 580 23439 8

GLOSSARY

Acid	A substance with a sour taste and a pH of less than 7. Contains excess hydrogen ions and reacts with a base to form a salt.
Adsorption	The adhesion of molecules to the surface of a solid (contrasting with *absorption*, where the molecules enter the body of the solid).
Aerobic	Requiring the presence of oxygen. In aerobic exercises, the muscles are never deprived of oxygen.
Albumin	A water-soluble protein found in egg whites etc. Coagulates with heat. Used for fining.
Aldehyde	A substance with the –CHO group, typified by acetaldehyde, a strong-smelling compound produced during the oxidation of wine.
Alkali	A substance with a pH greater than 7 and typified by the –OH group. Forms a salt with an acid. (*Syn.* base)
Amino acids	An organic acid containing the –NH$_2$ group. The building blocks of proteins. Synthesised by living cells or obtained from the diet.
Anaerobic	The absence of oxygen.
Anthocyanins	Soluble polyphenolic pigments in plants, ranging from red to blue. Colours change with pH.
Antioxidant	A substance that minimises the effect of oxidation by reacting with oxygen.
Aqueous	Relating to water
Archimedes screw	A broad-threaded screw encased in a tube. Originally used to raise water.

Atmosphere	The mass of air surrounding the earth, consisting approximately of 78% nitrogen and 21% oxygen. Also a unit of pressure of 14.7 pounds per square inch
Atom	The smallest particle of an element.
Atomic weight	The mass of one atom of an element.
Bacterium	Single-cell micro-organism, smaller than a yeast. *Pl.* bacteria.
Bar	One atmosphere, or 14.7 pounds per square inch (psi)
Bentonite	An aluminosilicate clay $Al_4Si_8O_{20}(OH)_4.nH_2O$ that swells in water and has powerful properties of adsorption.
Biochemical	Involving chemical reactions in living organisms.
Bronze	An alloy of copper and tin, of varying proportions.
Buffering effect	The ability of dissolved salts to affect the pH of a liquid.
Carcinogen	A substance that can initiate cancer.
Casein	A colloidal protein occurring in milk. Plays a part in the prevention of curdling. Used for fining wine.
Casse	From the French: breakage. A solid breaking out of solution. A precipitate.
Catalyst	A substance that enables a chemical reaction to proceed at a faster rate, but does not take part.
Chlorophyll	The green coloured substance in plants that enables the process of photosynthesis.
Colloid	A substance whose particles are too small to be visible to the naked eye, but whose molecules are much larger than simple molecules.

Complex	A substance formed by the loose association of two or more chemical compounds.
Decomposition	Breaking up into constituent parts.
Density	The mass of a substance per unit volume.
Distillate	The liquid collected from the condenser during a distillation process.
E-number	The code number given by the EU to food additives.
Enzyme	Biochemical catalyst, mostly proteins.
Epoxy resin	A tough resistant paint which sets by polymerisation of two components.
Esters	Fragrant compounds formed by reaction between an alcohol and an acid. e.g. ethyl acetate
Fermentation	A biochemical reaction involving enzymes
Flocculate	A loose deposit formed from aggregated cells
Free-run juice	The juice that runs out of a crushed grape without the application of pressure
Fructose	Occurs in fruits. Molecular formula $C_6H_{12}O_6$ but atoms are arranged as mirror image of glucose.
Glucose	The major sugar in the blood of higher animals. Molecular formula $C_6H_{12}O_6$ Also called dextrose.
Heat exchanger	A device for rapidly raising or lowering the temperature of a liquid.
Hydrolysis	Chemical decomposition with water.
Ion	An atom or molecule that has lost or gained electrons and thus possesses an electrostatic charge.

Isinglass	A pure form of gelatine obtained from the swimbladder of the sturgeon.
Isomers	Molecules that contain the same atoms, but in a different structural formation.
Ketone	Compounds typified by acetone. In wines generally one of the products of oxidation.
Kieselguhr	A diatomaceous earth used as a filter aid.
Lees	The solid deposit at the bottom of a vat.
Leguminous plants	Plants whose seeds are contained in pods. Most harbour nitrifying bacteria on their roots.
Lipoprotein	A substance that contains both fat and protein.
Maceration	Steeping solids in liquids to soften them
Marginal climate	A climate that barely exceeds the minimum requirements for growth. Can produce high quality.
Metabolism	The processing of a substance by a living organism.
Meta-stable	Having a small margin of stability
Microbiology	The science of microscopic life forms
Microclimate	The local climate of a small area
Micro-organism	Organism of microscopic size: yeast, bacteria, virus
Minerals	Naturally occurring substances containing important salts of metals
Molecular weight	The mass of one molecule of a substance. Calculated from the sum of the individual atomic weights.
Molecule	The smallest particle of a substance that retains the characteristic properties of the substance
Must	Unfermented or partially fermented grape juice

Nitrifying bacteria	Bacteria that convert atmospheric nitrogen to nitrogen compounds, e.g. nitrates. The 'fixing' of nitrogen.
Noble rot	Botrytis cinerea, pourriture noble, Edelfäule
Oenologist	A wine scientist (Gk *oinos* wine). Also sp. enologist.
Organic	Relating to living organisms and based on the chemistry of carbon
Oxidation	Reactions involving the combination of molecules with oxygen. (Strictly, the removal of electrons.)
Pathogen	An organism that causes disease.
Pectin	A gelatinous substance that binds together adjacent cell walls in plant tissue
Pectolytic enzyme	A enzyme that destroys pectin by hydrolysis.
Photosynthesis	The process by which light energy is used to convert carbon dioxide to carbohydrates.
Phytoalexin	A natural antibiotic that plants produce when under stress.
Planting density	The number of vines per unit area.
Polymerisation	The process by which molecules join together.
Polyphenols	A large group of compounds including the tannins and the anthocyanins. Some are powerful antioxidants.
Potassium bi-tartrate	HOOC.CHOH.CHOH.COOK Potassium hydrogen tartrate; Cream of Tartar. The substance of most tartrate crystal deposits.
Potassium metabisulphite	$K_2S_2O_5$ A white powder and a useful source of sulphur dioxide.
Precipitate	A solid that has been thrown out of solution.
Press juice	The juice that is extracted from grapes by pressure.

Proteins	Complex substances built up from amino acids. An important component of living tissue.
PVPP	Poly-vinyl poly-pyrrolidone, a manufactured polymer (plastic). It is a gentle fining which removes phenolic compounds from wine.
Reduction	The opposite of oxidation: a chemical reaction involving a dissociation from oxygen. (Strictly, the addition of electrons.)
Salt	A chemical compound formed by reaction between an acid and a base. Common salt or sodium chloride NaCl is but one example of a salt.
Solubility	The degree by which a solid will dissolve in a liquid.
Stomata	The openings in the surface of a leaf by which the plant breathes.
Sucrose	$C_{12}H_{24}O_{12}$ The sugar of beet and cane.
Sugars	A group of water soluble compounds of various degrees of sweetness.
Tannins	Colourless polyphenols that impart a bitter taste to wine, tea and other foodstuffs.
Tartaric acid	The most abundant acid in grape juice. The strongest of the acids of wine.
Titration	The process of the determination of the concentration of a dissolved substance by the addition of measured quantities of a suitable reactant.
Viscosity	The resistance to flow in a liquid.
Volatile	Easily vaporised
Yeast	A single cell micro-organism that reproduces by budding. *Saccharomyces cerevisiae* is the variety used for the majority of wine fermentations.

CONCLUSION

The great fascination of the study of the technology of winemaking is the realisation that there is no single right way of doing it. At every stage there are options open to the winemaker. Decisions have to be made, very often with no scientific evidence to help. Good wine is made by the intelligent winemaker who knows the grapes, who knows the effects of the various treatments and who knows what is wanted of the ultimate wine.

The potential quality of wine is present in the grapes when they are picked. "Good wine is made in the vineyard." The application of the principles of good quality control and quality assurance will ensure that the potential of the grape is upheld until the wine is consumed.

Despite the help that science can give to the art of winemaking, there can be no doubt that the winemaker is an artist, moulding the transformation of grape juice into one of those rare things that can give both pleasure and health, and whose study gives infinite rewards.

Drink wine, and you will sleep well.
Sleep, and you will not sin.
Avoid sin, and you will be saved.
Ergo, drink wine and be saved.

Medieval German

INDEX